L-Plate Boating

L-Plate Boating

Geoffrey Lewis
&
Tom McManus

SGM
Publishing

ISBN 978-0-9564536-0-0

Illustrations © Marlene Keeble 2010

Printed and bound in the UK by
CPI Anthony Rowe, Chippenham SN14 6LH

First published in Great Britain in 2010 by

SGM Publishing
47 Silicon Court, Shenley Lodge, Milton Keynes, Bucks MK5 7DJ
info@sgmpublishing.co.uk
www.sgmpublishing.co.uk

For Pam and Ray,
the two ladies whose tolerance and support
made this book possible

About Tom (Mac) McManus

Tom (Mac) McManus was born and raised in Harefield, Middlesex, close to the Grand Union Canal. As a child in the 1950s and '60s, he would often slip away to the nearby lock to watch the boats, sometimes earning a 'tanner' (six old pence) for helping them work through and riding down to the next lock with them.

He spent most of his working life in the motor trade, as a mechanic and, latterly, MoT tester, retaining an abiding interest in the canals throughout. After marrying Pam, his second wife, and moving to Milton Keynes with his job, that interest resurfaced – they borrowed a boat for a weekend, and found themselves hooked! After many years of hire-boat holidays, they eventually bought their first boat, Calico; after their children had flown the nest, he and Pam sold their house and moved aboard permanently, living at Cosgrove for a number of years and helping as crew on the local passenger boat, then owned and run by co-author Geoffrey Lewis. A keen sportsman, Mac has been an instructor in swimming and life-saving; he achieved a black belt in karate, which he has also taught.

Since taking early retirement, Mac and Pam have given up their mooring and now cruise the canals all year round, selling books and memorabilia at waterways events and tourist spots from their present boat, Mona Lisa. *L-Plate Boating* includes many of his reminiscences about their travels as well as the stories of their acquisition of Calico.

About Geoffrey Lewis

Geoffrey Lewis was born in Oxford, in 1947. Educated at the City's High School, and Hatfield University (then a polytechnic), he has since followed a varied career, including spells as a research chemist, security guard, and professional photographer. After many years in the motor trade, and eight years as the owner and captain of a canal-based passenger boat, he is now semi-retired and concentrating upon writing.

The author, Geoffrey Lewis, on the *Nutfield*

After a childhood spent close to the Oxford Canal, his love of the waterways led him to live aboard a narrowboat on the Grand Union Canal for sixteen years. Now back on dry land, he lives in Milton Keynes, within easy reach of the towpath, and recently took on the duties of Captain on the historic pair – *Nutfield* and *Raymond* – which are to be seen at many waterways events throughout the year.

Photographer, bell-ringer, real ale drinker, and American car enthusiast, he is currently engaged upon a number of new writing projects including more stories set in the working days of England's canals.

Chapter 1

L-Plate Boating

By Mac

Is this what it's all about? I think to myself as I stand in the hatchway of the boat looking down the canal from Cosgrove towards the Iron Trunk aqueduct. The sky is black and it's obviously going to chuck it down with rain again any moment; it seems that winter is going to last forever this year. It's late May and we are still having to light the fire most evenings and apart from a few bright days it seems that the rain has persisted almost non-stop since about October last year.

With these thoughts in my head my mind wanders back about twenty years to our first trip on a narrowboat. Although I grew up in Harefield near the Grand Union Canal and had, as a child, sneaked away to watch the working boats and sometimes work the locks for a "tanner" (six old pence) I had never steered a boat myself. My wife, Pam, had just started working for a construction company, and the managing director had bought a narrowboat with no real idea of what he was going to do with it. He finally decided that he would allow his employees to use it as long as they replaced any fuel they used. Pam had often heard me talking about my days "on the cut" – unfortunately, I probably gave the impression that I knew more about boating than I actually did, so she had booked the boat for the following weekend, telling the owner of the boat not to worry about any instruction as her husband was an expert boater.

As the weekend approached I found myself looking forward to our adventure with a mixture of anticipation and growing trepidation. I had tried to tell Pam that I was a little rusty at boat handling and that a short period of instruction might not be a bad idea, but she brushed this idea aside with her usual enthusiasm, saying "don't worry, you'll be fine". Finally the fateful day dawned and we made our way to Baxters Wharf at Yardley Gobion to meet Keith Baxter, who was to hand over the boat to us. He showed us to the boat and asked whether I would like any instruction. Before Pam could say "no" I gratefully said that I thought this would be a good idea. So while Pam and our two children, Michelle and Iain, aged about three and two respectively, loaded our bits and pieces onto the boat Keith showed me how to check the oil and water, operate the stern tube greaser, start and stop the engine and operate the gears. These instructions were gratefully received and gave me a little more confidence to tackle our first "voyage".

We had wanted to extend the weekend by picking up the boat on Friday evening, so it was decided that we would make our way to Cosgrove and moor there for the night. Then on the Saturday we would cruise until early afternoon before turning to start our return journey. This was to ensure that we would not have to rush in order to get back by Sunday evening. We had no idea when we set off in high spirits on our adventure that this plan would fall apart dramatically over the next twenty-four hours!

An hour later we arrived at Cosgrove. Our first problem presented itself very suddenly when we realised that although Keith had been very helpful with his advice, he had assumed that we would be able to deal with a small thing like coming to the side and tying up. With the lock now in sight and the moorings sliding past we decided that we had no choice but to stop somehow. In the true tradition of boating we gave up trying to work out a proper technique and used the "trust to luck" method. I slowed the boat to tickover, pointed the front towards the bank and instructed Pam to get off the front end with the front rope as we got to the side. I then stepped nonchalantly off the back with the stern rope, leaving Michelle and Ian in the boat, and we tried to tie up. Unfortunately, however, I had forgotten to take the boat out of gear. We were dragged unceremoniously along the bank for some distance before I realised my mistake and managed to leap back on board and rectify the situation.

After looking round Cosgrove for a while we had our first meal aboard the boat and settled down for an early night. Well,

that was the plan, but in fact we got very little sleep and were all up at the crack of dawn, chomping at the bit at an hour that was definitely not suited to starting a noisy diesel engine. We decided to have our breakfast before we left, not because we were hungry but because we would almost certainly have been found dead or mutilated beyond recognition in the lock if we had set off at such an ungodly hour! Finally we decided that we would chance moving on and started the engine. It was then that our next problem became evident. I had used locks many years previously and was fairly confident that I could manage fairly well, but unfortunately Pam had never seen a lock before, and she was not keen to take charge of the boat. We decided that we would look at the lock while the engine warmed up and formulate a plan to deal with said obstacle. After a short discussion we set the lock and I went back to get the boat.

I approached the lock with trepidation, convinced that we would do something seriously wrong and sink the boat. What actually happened was unbelievable. I took the boat into the lock and stopped it well before hitting the far gate and Pam shut the gate gently behind me. She then proceeded to do what she has done so many times since. She worked the lock at her own pace, refusing to work any faster than she wanted to, opening paddles, watching the boat and finally opening the bottom gate, all as if she had been doing it all her life! Whilst we negotiated the lock I kept the children with me in the hatchway, where they could learn safely about locks. In later years as they grew older and stronger they were both to take their turn at locking and running the boat.

We left the lock and set off on the next leg of our journey with a feeling of satisfaction and anticipation which we have experienced many times since. A few minutes later we crossed the Iron Trunk aqueduct over the river Ouse, amazed at the view and even more amazed at the structure itself. No matter how many times I cross this wonder of engineering I never cease to be impressed by it.

We felt by this time that we were truly on an adventure, and as we travelled serenely along we had the same feelings that we still enjoy when we travel on new waters: Wondering what is round the next bend, and gazing in wonderment at all the beauty that is missed when travelling at much greater speeds in a car. As we passed under the bridge at the Old Wolverton road, with the Galleon pub seemingly perched at the top, we slowly made our way into the outskirts of Wolverton past the rear of the British Rail works, and the whole scene changed dramatically in the space of a few moments. The appearance changed from tranquil, open countryside to noisy industrial bustle as we made our way past an almost unbroken wall of buildings for what seemed to be miles. In fact it was about half a mile, but our slow pace made it seem much longer. I had driven past the front of "The Works" countless times since moving to the area in the mid seventies and had often wondered at the size of the place which, at the time, was the central repair depot for the entire rail network, but the magnitude of the operation was truly incredible from our boat which had seemed so big to us as we negotiated the turns and bridges, but now seemed so tiny, dwarfed as it was by the huge buildings.

We passed under bridge 69 which we found out many years later was known by the old boatmen and the locals as Suicide Bridge. I have tried to research the origins of this name but can only find a reference to a woman who was reported to have committed suicide from the bridge while her son was serving in the army during the First World War. There is no mention of how this could be achieved from a bridge that is only about fifteen feet above the water! A real mystery.

As we passed under the next two bridges, built very closely together, we felt that the buildings would go on forever, but we were surprised that a short distance after the next bridge, the road bridge at Wolverton, they stopped as quickly as they had appeared and we were, once again, in open countryside. We soon approached the derelict windmill on the outskirts of New Bradwell. I was pleased to see that work had begun on the restoration of this beautiful landmark and now, many years later, I am grateful that it was saved from almost total ruin and restored to its former beauty.

Moments later we passed the New Inn and soon rounded Target Turn, so named I was told because the soldiers during the threat of Napoleonic invasion would use the passing boats for target practice from their ranges in the old Bradwell Abbey. We passed under the bridge and on by the Black Horse, recently and idiotically renamed the Proud Perch before thankfully reverting to its original name.

And so on with our journey which took us now past Great Linford, with its lovely church standing proudly on the hill, looking down at us, past Coopers Wharf, where the old Newport Pagnell arm used to run into the old town, and on through the countryside where the new town of Milton Keynes was just being born. How this area was to change over the next few years with the growth of this town! Although, I have to say, the canal today is as lovely as it was then, a credit to the planners and people of the area.

Onwards we went through the quiet, unspoiled countryside until, eventually, we came to our next lock at Fenny Stratford, on the outskirts of Bletchley. There seemed to be very little point to this lock, with a drop of only twelve inches, and it was many years before I found out that it was only built to help to prevent water loss by shortening the pound between Cosgrove and the next lock at Stoke Hammond (Talbot's Lock), almost three miles further on. This would have made the original pound nearly fourteen miles long. Once through Stoke Hammond lock we came across our first flight of locks, Soulbury three, with the beautiful old pub halfway up. Once through here we decided that it was time to start thinking about turning round ready for our return journey, which we were going to start that day and finish at a nice leisurely pace on the Sunday.

As I said earlier, how our plans were to come adrift! Borne along on the euphoria of our adventure we hadn't considered how or where we were going to carry out the tricky manoeuvre of turning a seventy foot narrowboat around in a forty-foot wide canal. Up to this point it had not been too difficult to handle, our only manoeuvring being moving forwards, stopping at the locks and mooring up the night before, which had made me more confident than I should have been.

Firstly we had to find a "winding hole", a term I had never even heard of until we looked in our Nicholson's guide, which someone had fortunately left on the boat. The guide showed one at Old Linslade, a short distance further on, so we thought that this would be perfect – and so it would have been if we had not gone straight past it. You see, the unfortunate thing is that the guide only told us where it was, not how to identify it, and, as we had no idea what a "winding hole" looked like, we didn't know what we were looking for. Assuming that there would be a sign of some kind to tell us, on we went until it was obvious, when we came to Leighton Lock, that we had missed it. At this point we weren't too concerned because the guide showed another one a little way above the lock, so on we went again looking for a sign to tell us about the elusive "winding hole". Unfortunately not only was it again not signposted, but it was actually at the Wyvern Shipping Company's base so, once again, past we went in our ignorance.

Now we were really worried, thinking that maybe some prankster had given us a dodgy guide and that we would have to go all the way to Brentford before we could turn round. Then Pam had a brainwave; she noticed that the next winding hole was just after the next bridge, the Town Bridge, surely we couldn't miss that! We slowed right down and stopped under the bridge to check things out and then Pam said "there it is", pointing at what appeared to be a wall on the other side of the canal. At last the penny dropped; a winding hole is not a signposted special place, just a wide piece of the canal! At last, we could turn, or so we thought.

At this point two things conspired to prevent said turn. Firstly my lack of boating skills meant that precise manoeuvring was to be impossible, and secondly the water level in the pound was very low after a hot summer, so that as I put the front end across the canal we suddenly stopped as we ran on to the mud. When I say stopped, the front end stopped dead and the back end started to swing round, so that after the initial shock of our abrupt halt, it appeared that we would make it after all. We were not to be that lucky. The back end swung more and more swiftly round until it too suddenly stopped and the engine stalled as the propeller clawed its way into the mud leaving us stranded broadside across the canal. My first action was to restart the engine and drive off the mud, but as soon as I put the boat in gear it stalled, convincing me that I had terminally damaged several thousand pounds worth of someone else's property. Eventually it dawned on me that the true reason for our lack of movement was that something was stuck around the propeller. A look in the weed hatch confirmed my suspicions; there *was* something around the prop – the bottom of the canal! After the initial shock and a few choice words from Pam followed by the comment from Michelle "do we have to spend the night here?" a horrible feeling of dread started to wash over me as our true predicament became apparent. As far as I could tell we were well and truly aground and I had no idea how to release us.

We quickly adopted the methods used by countless others before us, attempting to push ourselves off with poles, with as little luck as most of our predecessors, and Michelle's prophesy about an overnight stop seemed to be becoming an ominous possibility. After several useless attempts I became aware that we were not alone. As I looked around I saw several boats waiting patiently on either side of us with more arriving every minute or two, and quite a crowd gathering on the bridge above us watching eagerly. Our efforts became almost hysterical as we attempted, unsuccessfully, to restore navigation to the navigation. As we neared exhaustion with no apparent hope of freedom, the man on the first boat below us asked quite calmly "would you like some help?"

Would I like some help? At this point I would probably have sold my soul to the devil in order to get free of the mud holding us in front of our ever swelling audience, so I answered politely "yes please". His first suggestion was to try and pull us back in the direction in which we had come but I was terrified that if we didn't turn here we would never turn at all so I asked him if there was any possibility of trying to continue the turn. He obligingly

16

said he would try and, after enlisting the help of a boat from the other side of our makeshift dam, he tied his front rope to our bow and the other boat's rope to our stern and they proceeded to drag us across the mud. Within a few minutes we were free, much to the relief of the other boaters and the obvious merriment of the people on the bridge, who raised a thunderous cheer. The channel was reopened to the very patient boaters, we apologised profusely and pulled over to allow them all to go in front of us before setting off on our homeward journey.

As it was now early evening we decided that it would be best to make our way back as far as possible, in order to allow us as much time as possible on the Sunday in which to make the return journey. We reasoned that it would take us at least as long as the outward trip and we did not relish the idea of having to rush any more than was necessary, so we carried on until dusk started to enfold us. We found ourselves a short distance above the three locks at Soulbury, so the journey the next day would be fairly straightforward, we thought.

As it transpired, this was to be the only correct assumption we had made that day. Exhausted, we settled down for our evening meal and a good rest, and Pam did something else that she has continued to do over the years. It seemed that I had barely finished tying up the boat before my dinner was on the table. Not bad after a days hard boating.

The following morning dawned bright and sunny and the previous day's trials were put behind us as we set off bright and early, after a quick breakfast. If we thought that the return trip would be boring, having travelled the same route on the outward journey, we were soon proved wrong. Again, as has proven to be the case many times over the years, the same route is not the same journey twice running. Everything appears different when travelling in the other direction, or at different times of the year. We were in no particular rush as we had agreed with Keith Baxter that we would lock the boat and leave it on his wharf if he had gone by the time we returned, an arrangement which proved very useful under the circumstances.

In contrast to the events of the previous afternoon, everything ran smoothly throughout the day. Pam seemed even less rushed at the locks, seeing us through in her by now usual easy going way, and she even took a turn at steering the boat, although she was not as happy doing this. I didn't mind at all because I was as happy then as I am all these years later when I am at the helm, slowly meandering through the country side, daydreaming most of the time.

All too soon we arrived at Cosgrove lock and decided to stop one last time for a quick cuppa before cruising the last hour to Yardley Gobion. Our mooring procedure had improved considerably since we had passed through two days previously, and we must have seemed quite experienced by this time as we brought the boat gently to the side and tied it up without any fuss, even remembering to take it out of gear. It was a shame that there was no-one to admire our expertise!

Many years later, an old boating friend of ours observed that he could always tell when a manoeuvre was going to go wrong, because there would always be an audience to watch the mayhem, while if everything was going to go well he would always be alone. It was no good, he mentioned, talking about his skilful boating in the pub because, like the fisherman's "the one that got away" there would be no witnesses to corroborate his stories.

The last part of the adventure went without incident and we were soon moored at Baxters Wharf, unloading the boat and making our way back to our little house, which seemed huge after the confines of a seventy foot narrowboat. Since that first journey we have spent many times, both happy and not so happy, on hired boats.

We eventually bought our own boat, finally giving up our house to live permanently "on the cut" – but that is the stuff of other stories! So:

Is this what it's all about? I think to myself as I stand in the hatchway of the boat looking down towards the Iron Trunk aqueduct. The sky is black and it has just started to chuck it down with rain.

The answer is obvious to me as I duck back inside the boat and shut the hatch.

Chapter 2

In the Cut

By Geoff

I'd met up with some friends for a fortnight's holiday boating, me with my little forty-four foot Barney, and them in a Wyvern hire-boat. 'They' consisted of husband and wife, two daughters and a twelve-year-old son, who I shall call Richard for the purposes of my tale. He had decided that he would accompany me on my boat, I suspect to escape the depredations of two older sisters, for the duration of the trip.

We'd set off from Cosgrove, where I was moored at the time, up the Junction to Braunston, up the northern Oxford to Sutton's, up the Coventry to Fazeley Turn, right through Birmingham and down the Worcester cut to King's Norton and then back via Lapworth and Hatton. An enjoyable evening in the Cape of Good Hope, and the next morning we were about to set off down the two Cape locks and back in the direction of Braunston. The other crew were getting ready to fire up the engine and loose off the lines; I started mine as Richard cast off the fore-end line. I untied the stern, dropped the clutch in and steered gently out from the bank; Richard gave the front of the cabin a good push so that I would clear the stern of another boat tied in front of us.

I looked back over my shoulder to see if the others were following; turning back again, I saw no sight of Richard but assumed he'd jumped in to the well-deck. Until, that is, I spotted him clambering out onto the towpath beside the boat, to the accompaniment of loud and raucous laughter from his family behind me. I pulled in again, and stood him in the shower to drain quietly while his sisters, grinning hugely, went to set the first lock for us.

You've guessed, I know. He'd performed that hilariously inevitable feat which we've all achieved at some time – pushed the boat out and reached and passed that point of no return where you are stretched from bank to boat with no possibility of

recovering in either direction. I simply hadn't heard the splash over the noise of my aged Sabb twin.

There aren't many boaters out there who haven't been in the cut at some point in time. Not, perhaps, the old folks from the days of trade – born and raised on boats, they have a much better developed sense of self-preservation, water-wise, than the present generation of pleasure boaters. And as a character in my novel 'A Girl At The Tiller' says, 'We troy not ter fall in, it tends ter 'old the boats oop'. But if a modern-day boater tells you they haven't ever fallen in, treat that tale with a degree of suspicion! Personally, I've lost count.

I used to run a trip-boat – you know, 'Trips around the bay in the Saucy Sue' as you might have seen in an old Giles cartoon. Except that we didn't go around the bay, being based on the Grand Union Canal, and the boat wasn't called Saucy Sue. There was a Saucy Sue locally – another trip boat, which ran out of High House Wharf, a bit further north up the canal. But that's another story. No, my boat was the Linda, an old (1912) Josher motor with a nice little bar and seats for forty passengers, converted in the 1950s.

It was a warm summer day in the late 1990s. We were running public trips from Cosgrove, down over the Iron Trunk Aqueduct to Old Wolverton and back. After the second, I'd turned the boat ready to go again and pulled in on the old sand wharf which was our base of operations, pleased to see that a small queue had developed while we were out. My crew, a likely lad by the name of John, jumped off to tie the fore-end; I took the stern line, dropped it over the dolly and stepped off. Threading it through the ring on the wharf, I turned and stepped back onto the boat.

Except that I hadn't noticed that, as John had pulled the fore-end in, the stern had swung out. Not a lot – just enough that my questing toes barely managed to reach the edge of the cants on the counter. The water isn't too deep by Cosgrove Wharf – it only came up to my waist. I climbed out, pulling myself up by the dollies onto the counter and stepping back, more carefully this time, onto the bank and retrieving the rope to hold the stern in while the passengers disembarked and the new lot got on. All this time, John had been performing his duties impeccably, seeing the customers off safely and ushering the fresh ones aboard, with his back to me. I could have done without his question, as he turned around to see me standing there in a puddle of the water which was still draining out of my trousers:

'What on earth have you been doing?'

It's not always people, of course. A group of us had boated from Gayton Junction to the Old Wharf at Bugbrooke one summer's evening for a jovial meal and a few beers; returning to the boats, tied about four abreast on the pub landing, we were intending to congregate in one couple's lounge for coffee. Or maybe a whisky or three. This particular couple had a pretty little boat, with a nice front well-deck which had a canopy over a deck-board and plank in traditional fashion. They also had two dogs, which was why they had tied directly against the bank with our other boats on the outside.

They'd left the dogs inside while we were all in the pub – both sides of the canopy were rolled up, as it was a pleasant summer night. I'll call the lady in question Janet, which is actually my sister's name. No, it isn't you, dear – just go back to your knitting, and let me tell the story. Janet opened the cabin doors, and the dogs, who had by now probably been keeping their legs firmly crossed, came hurtling out. The Jack Russell leapt onto the bank and hurried to find a suitable bush. Unfortunately, the other one chose the wrong side of the boat.

It's not an easy task, finding a jet-black poodle in the dark waters of a canal at night, when you've all had a few drinks. Thankfully, someone had the sense to call for quiet and we were able to follow the frantic splashing sounds and fish the little beggar out, looking very bedraggled and sorry for itself.

Given some daylight, and a less urgent desire for freedom, dogs can be remarkably at home on boats. Another friend used to have a Lurcher, now sadly passed to that glorious dog-kennel in the sky, which would casually stroll around the gunwales of an old working motor. Not just around the cabin, but along the side of the hold as well, unerringly balanced, to the amazement of any onlookers. I'm sure it did it deliberately to show off, raising gasps of astonishment when the seemingly-inevitable splash never came.

Not all have quite the same ability, though. I used to know a Golden Retriever which was firmly convinced that it was human

– no great problem, except that it would sometimes forget to take its back legs along, which can present difficulties when getting on and off the boat. On more than one occasion, I've seen it step from the bank onto the counter and walk nonchalantly forward, only to disappear abruptly, bottom-first, over the side when its hindquarters reached the edge. It did this once in Stoke Bruerne locks, to the immense hilarity of the gathered gongoozlers, which was followed by another gale of laughter at the look of injured pride on its face when it was hauled unceremoniously out onto the side.

Sometimes the best boat-dogs can be fooled by circumstances. Another time, we were at Atherstone top lock, myself and a friend who I shall call Trevor, and his recently-acquired Labrador pup. It was late summer, and a mass of floating pond-weed had gathered in the lock-head, trapped against the gates; Trevor crossed over the balance-beams to the far side, but the pup obviously didn't like the look of this narrow passage and preferred the grassy plain beside it. The result was a very wet and startled Labrador, generously draped in green weed.

But don't be put off taking your pets on the boats with you – they can provide hours of harmless amusement. Just be sure to have an old and very large towel handy.

Chapter 3

A Boat of Our Own

By Mac

It hardly seemed possible, but here we were on our way to collect our first boat from the marina at Braunston. My wife, Pam, and I had talked about buying a narrowboat of our own ever since we had been bitten by the boating bug over twenty years earlier. Although our first voyage had been very eventful we had enjoyed it immensely and in the years since we had hired boats regularly from Wyvern Shipping in Leighton Buzzard and had become well and truly hooked. Eventually, by taking on extra jobs, we had saved enough to buy Calico, the craft we were now on our way to collect.

We had been looking for some time for a boat and had been to see several before Harold Barnet, an ex-boatman and friend of our childminder, had told us of this 'lovely little boat' moored at Cropredy.

He even went with Pam to have a look at it. The next thing I knew was that I received a phone call at work to say that she had found 'just the boat for us' and had agreed to buy it, securing the deal with a one thousand pound deposit! She must have sensed my astonishment, probably due to some of the expletives I now employed to bring to her attention that I did not think that handing over this vast sum of money was a very wise investment move, on the say so of an old man that we had only met a few days earlier.

She reassured me in her usual cheerful way by completely ignoring my pleas to retrieve the deposit, saying that if I did not like the boat, the owner, again a complete stranger, had promised that he would return it. I was less than convinced, and beginning to panic that our hard earned cash would disappear along with the boat and its owner as soon as they were out of her sight, but she, still happily convinced that she was right, completely ignored my ravings which were quickly becoming hysterical. Instead she told me in her best Michael Winner impression to 'calm down

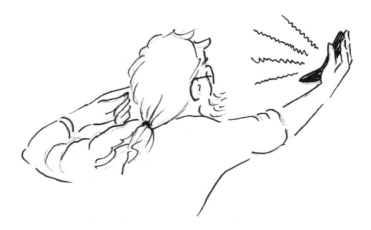

and listen to this'. What happened next was even more incredible than anything that had previously occurred – I had to tear the phone from my ear as it emitted a deafening noise which sounded to me like a series of explosions echoing inside an empty building. Eventually it all went quiet and I heard Pam speaking to me with the noise, a little quieter now, in the background.

"Isn't it wonderful?" she enquired. I was by now convinced that she had completely lost her mind as I summoned all my courage together to ask "what?"

"That was the engine" she announced excitedly "Harold says it's a Lister, a proper engine, isn't that great?" At this point something really strange happened. I found myself actually becoming quite calm as I realised that I had been right all those years. I was married to a mad woman who had just tried to deafen me with a mobile phone, given a thousand pounds to a complete stranger and, at best, bought a boat with a couple of bombs going off in the engine room.

I gave up and replied with the only comment appropriate to the moment: "Yes love, great".

When I arrived home that night it was impossible to miss Pam's excitement at having found our boat and I resigned myself to the fact that I would have to play along with her until the weekend, when we were to travel to Cropredy for me to cast my eye over our new acquisition. I tried really hard to hide my conviction that this would be a fruitless journey, ending in us looking at the empty section of canal where a boat called Calico had once sat.

Saturday morning dawned and the sun was shining as we drove through the lanes to Cropredy, parking outside the little shop, and Pam led me excitedly to the towpath:

"There" she said triumphantly, and we both gazed at the little boat moored just below the lock, she with great pride and me with horror. To my surprise Calico was still moored there but the sight that greeted my eyes was, to put it in the mildest terms, totally horrifying. To say that she had seen better days would have been an understatement akin to saying that World War Two was a bit of a scuffle. With paint that looked as if it had been applied when she was first made over thirty years previously and more rust than your average M.O.T. failure she looked less than appealing and it was with a huge effort that I pulled myself together and walked up to her.

The owner was not able to meet us but had left the keys with the mooring warden who now greeted us and opened the front doors to give us access to the interior. By this time I was almost convinced by Pam's happy chatter that the boat would be fine once we had given it a lick of paint and I stepped inside anticipating that the interior would be in a much better condition – after all the owner had been living on it until a few weeks before selling it. Wrong! To my absolute horror the interior was in an equally appalling condition to the faded and peeling outside, with a solid fuel fire full of old ash, a full toilet cassette, grime in the sink and a layer of dust on every surface which seemed to reduce the headroom by several inches.

As I felt myself starting to panic again I struggled, unsuccessfully, to find something positive to say about Calico despite feeling an overwhelming urge to leave, quickly. As I stepped back onto the bank I found myself praying that the vendor would stick to his word and give us back our deposit. Pam joined me and pointed out that I had not yet had a look at the engine. I could hardly contain myself as I wandered, with the mooring warden, to the back of the boat, where he opened the rear doors and we gazed in at the old two cylinder Lister engine, which I found myself regarding with fear and suspicion since our last encounter via the mobile phone. "Would you like to start it?" enquired our host.

No I bloody well wouldn't I thought as I replied "oh yes please" with what I hoped sounded like enthusiasm. The old engine was coaxed into life with surprising ease and seemed to be much quieter on this occasion, even starting to sound a bit (Just a bit) reassuring.

What happened next was perhaps the most astonishing thing that had happened that morning. I stood up on the rear deck, the old Lister banging away in front of my feet and looked along the roof of the boat with my arm resting on the tiller, and I was astounded to find that I felt completely relaxed and at home on the old girl.

I have often been told since that the boat that is for you will make itself known to you, and this is exactly how I felt at that moment. It was the beginning of a love affair which we shared for some years with this old lady of the canals, and one which lives with me even now.

In a better frame of mind, we drove home and started to make all the arrangements necessary for the final purchase of what we had now come to regard as "our boat". Fortunately we had no idea of the complexities of marine acquisition (buying a boat), not to mention the expense, for if we had I am sure that we would have proceeded no further, love affair or no love affair. Luckily I left the organisation of this process to Pam, because while she is excellent at these things I would have to be considered to be about as organised as a kite in the wind.

Over the next few days she found a surveyor and a boatyard in order that our pride and joy could be checked over properly by an expert, leaving us worry free as we continued with the venture. Unfortunately the term worry free seems to mean something completely different to my wife and myself. She adopts the attitude that once an arrangement has been made then that is the end of the matter, leaving someone else, usually me, to sort out the "little details". Among these was the small matter of the geographical difference between where the boat was moored at Cropredy and the selected boatyard at Braunston. As she observed when I pointed this small fact out to her:

"It can't be far. I've looked on the map, and it's only a couple of inches". Now I don't honestly believe that she was being serious, although I sometimes wonder, but it does show the difference between our attitudes. I worry about little details like this while she has the overwhelming confidence to assume that everything will work out. The most irritating thing is that she is nearly always right, as she was on this occasion.

While I ranted and raved about the impossibility of her proposals she made the impossible possible with a quick phone call to Calico's owner, persuading him not only to deliver the boat to Braunston for us but also to invite us to go with him on the first leg of the journey. I was astounded, not only with her cheek but also with the fact that in the same phone call she persuaded him to throw a new boat safety certificate into the deal, explaining to him that our surveyor had advised us that this should be an essential part of the process! Next it was the boatyard's turn to be clawed into her negotiations. I stopped listening as I heard her saying to the unfortunate recipient of her call:

"About the hull blacking, what sort of discount can we expect?"

Negotiations over and arrangements made we waited excitedly for the weekend to arrive and on the Saturday morning we again drove to Cropredy, collecting our skipper at Fenny Compton on the way, so that he could leave his car there in order to drop us back to Cropredy for ours at the end of the day. Our vehicles deposited around the Oxfordshire and Warwickshire countryside we stepped aboard with the owner for our first trip aboard the good ship Calico.

Again the sun was shining as we set off up through the lock and slid slowly through the peaceful village. Well it *was* peaceful until Calico's old Lister performed its usual trick of deafening most people within about twenty yards. It was especially noisy whenever we passed anything solid, such as a wall or a moored boat, and there were plenty of both on this tranquil weekend. Soon we had left the village behind, to the relief, I suspect, of the occupants of that slumbering hamlet, and proceeded to wake up the various wildlife of the countryside beyond. Birds in the trees and hedgerows, rabbits, sheep in the fields, nothing was left asleep that day as we clattered through this section of England's green and pleasant land. I am convinced that even the fish in that section of the Oxford canal are deaf to this day.

After a mile or so I was offered the tiller so that I could get a feel for the old lady, and as I had before I felt immediately at home as she seemed to almost steer herself through the beautiful Oxfordshire countryside. I thought nothing of the boat which I saw coming towards us, lost in my thoughts of the many days ahead when we would be cruising Britain's waterways, until an alarming sequence of events occurred. The first sign that something was not quite right presented itself when the steerer of the other boat began to hop about quite alarmingly, like some demented disco dancer, before disappearing from view completely. Now I am not easily frightened but the sight of this modern day Mary Celeste veering towards us unnerved me considerably. As I went into panic mode, putting Calico full astern to, hopefully, limit the impending impact another person appeared upon the deck of the careering vessel and proceeded to do the same. As we both came to a halt facing each other he said calmly:

"Sorry mate, I was inside having a pee. My friend didn't know what to do, and he panicked".

"He wasn't the only one!" I said as I reflected on the fact that at least *his* pee was in the correct receptacle.

The rest of the journey was uneventful and by mid afternoon we arrived at Fenny Compton where we left Calico moored near the Wharf pub, in readiness for the owner to take her on to Braunston. He had calculated that he would be able to get to Napton the following day, leaving the boat there while he was at work during the week, then on to Braunston the following weekend.

It was decided that the survey would be carried out early in the week following Calico's arrival at the boatyard, the surveyor having told us that he would be available. Everything looked rosy on that sunny afternoon and I was feeling much better as we said goodbye to our host at Cropredy and drove home, chatting excitedly about our plans for the days and years ahead, cruising the inland waterways on our little boat. After all, there could be no more surprises, all that was needed was for the surveyor to cast an eye over her and for the boatyard to apply a couple of coats of bitumen to the hull and we would be off down the Grand Union canal to Gayton Junction, where Pam had organised us a mooring. But that feeling of self-assurance was not to last...

Now that the purchase was almost complete, we thought, the time seemed to drag until the day of the survey, but at last the time came for us to drive over to Braunston to meet our surveyor, who seemed quite pleased that I had booked the day off work to discuss his findings with him. Had I known how nerve racking this was to be I would not have been so eager! Upon arrival we went into the marina office and we were introduced to our surveyor, who was much younger than I had expected, and off we went to the dry dock to begin the inspection. On the way he asked me how much I knew about boats and put me at my ease when he explained that the question had only been asked so that he could determine how basic his explanation of the survey process would be. Having ascertained that I probably knew more about yak herding than boats, he explained in very simple terms that he would be inspecting every part of the boat and I was soon lost in the list of items to be checked. I understood about the hull, gas and basic electrical systems, but stern gear, integral water tanks, paloma heaters, inverters and a seemingly endless list of other strangely named items were a complete mystery to me.

However, he seemed more than competent and I was happy to allow him to "cast an eye" over her until, to my absolute horror, he produced a large hammer and started to hit the hull in various places. He must have sensed my trepidation, probably due to the terrified expression which I was unable to hide, because he said quite calmly "don't worry the steel's good and thick" before carrying on with his noisy work. I was happy(!) to accept that he knew what he was doing and reasoned that he wouldn't do anything to actually harm the old girl, but when he produced a small angle grinder I needed further reassurance before he could carry on. After all how was I to know that he was only going to remove some small areas of paint? I had no idea what was involved in the process of carrying out an ultra sound check and he had to explain to me that all he was doing was checking the thickness of the steel.

After this the rest of the survey seemed a lot less stressful with our engineer explaining everything to us as he checked the rest of the items on his list, which seemed endless to me, finishing with a pressure test of the gas system. The whole process took most of the day and I found myself becoming most impressed with his attention to detail. As he worked he stopped from time to time and used a voice recorder to make notes of his findings and at the end of the inspection he informed us that he would send us a written report in a few days time. Before he finished he gave us a list if the items which would have to be attended to before he would issue a safety certificate and offered to give a copy of the list to the boatyard so that they could negotiate with the vendor to get this work attended to. I was relieved that he had not found any major faults with the boat and as we set off home I was more than relieved that the day was over.

True to his word he sent us the written report of his survey and my heart stopped as I opened what appeared to me to be a copy of War and Peace, containing endless pages of items that needed attention. At this point I felt, as most people who are buying a boat for the first time must feel, that we had made a huge mistake, but Pam came to the rescue once again and provided a very simple solution – she phoned the surveyor, who was patience itself as he explained everything very carefully, eventually drawing my attention to the final note on the survey, which assured us that the boat was sound and worth what we were paying for it. I thanked him again for his help and having finished the call I left it to Pam to contact the boatyard and the owner to finalise the deal.

A few days later we received a call to inform us that the boatyard had finished the work and that our new boat safety certificate had been issued. The following Saturday we set off and it hardly seemed possible that we were on our way collect *our* boat from the boatyard at Braunston for our first independent cruise of the canal...

Chapter 4

Braunston Tunnel

By Geoff

It was a cold spring day, and we had about 35 tons on the pair. Bagged coal, headed around from Nether Heyford on the Grand Junction to the Thames, via Oxford. The afternoon was getting on; we'd run up Buckby onto the summit and were heading, full bracket, for Braunston Tunnel and the flight down into the village where we'd tie for the night. Well, as near full bracket as you can these days when the bottom's much too near the top for loaded boats.

We'd passed Blisworth Tunnel earlier in the day, before loading, so we approached the next hole in the ground with no trepidation. A hundred yards short of the entrance, a slow-moving pleasure boat waved us past; very generous of him, especially as he managed to run himself well and truly aground under the trees on the off-side in the process! So we headed for the darkness, a bit off-line to the left of the cut. I was steering, with our captain beside me on the gunwale; he reached inside for the switch and turned on the headlight – next thing, the fore-end disappeared into the tunnel.

It takes a moment or two for your eyes to get used to things, before you can see the light from the lamp on the brickwork – but it seemed to be taking longer than usual...

'B****r me – b****y 'eadlight's not workin'!' Captain's comment rather agreed with my own conclusion. Now any sensible modern boater would just stop and back carefully out, and then effect repairs – but you can't exactly stop and back up when you've got around thirty tons of butty heading very rapidly for your stern end. If you try, the collision would be quite spectacular, to say nothing of eighty feet of good hemp line wrapped all around the blades. So, with no obvious other option, I carried on.

''Ang on – I'll go an' see if it's a loose wire.'

At this point I grew a little concerned. Staying in the middle of a tunnel in the pitch dark, with no form of illumination, is not the easiest of tasks. And Captain was a rather portly gentleman, which only served to increase quite markedly the possibility that I would wipe him off against the bricks as he endeavoured to clamber around the cabin on the gunwales.

However, he made it. After a brief expedition to the fore-end, he returned, passing safely around the cabinside once more by some miraculous feat of agility.

We still had no headlight:

'Can't find anything wrong' he breathlessly informed me: ''Ave you got a torch?'

A short discussion revealed that the only other light on the boat was the lamp on the old bike we used for lock-wheeling. Both bike and lamp were in somewhat dubious condition, but off he set to retrieve it. Rather to our amazement, it proved to work when he switched it on – but although it might have been adequate to illumine the towpath at short range, it was hardly up to the job of lighting a loaded pair through a mile and a quarter of tunnel. And the oil-lamp on the butty's fore-end didn't help much, either, from eighty feet away behind us. But as I've said, we had little choice in the matter.

By now we were some way beneath the surrounding countryside, clattering along at quite a good speed despite having no forward vision at all. Except, that is, for the other headlight approaching us from the opposite direction...

What the unfortunate fellow at the helm of the hire-boat must have thought when he realised that an old working-boat was hurtling towards him with no lights I daren't imagine. Especially as, by the time his light showed me enough of the tunnel to see where I was, we were well and truly on the wrong side. It was far too late for me to get seventy feet of Josher across the tunnel – you have to give the hire-boater credit for adapting to the

situation and going around us in the face of what he would have been told about passing on the right in tunnels. But our relief was short-lived when we saw him pass us and then turn to cross in front of the butty.

I don't know if our frantic shouting and waving attracted his attention, or if it was the sight of the bowstring-tight towline which made him decide that that was not a good idea. Either way, he swerved sharply back onto the wrong side, and scraped past the butty as well. I imagine he's still dining out on the tale to this day.

Chapter 5

Truly Ours

By Mac

At last, we felt, Calico was truly ours, and as we drove to the marina to collect her I reflected on the events of the last few weeks since she had been surveyed. The surveyor had compiled a long list of "little jobs" which had kept the marina engineers occupied for this period, and Pam had amassed a huge pile of paperwork relating to our latest acquisition. From mooring applications to insurance documents and boat safety certificates to boat licence forms, it seemed that we would soon have a mountain of paper larger than the vessel itself! Then there were the ever spiralling costs. It seemed that every time she picked up the phone to enquire about something, someone wanted to take money off us and I was reminded of the acronym B.O.A.T, Bring Over Another Thousand.

However, as I drove through the beautiful Northamptonshire countryside I felt very happy to be on our way to start our first voyage aboard our own boat. Our son, Iain, had decided to come with us and we had enlisted the help of Harold Barnet, the man who had first found Calico for sale at Cropredy. We had met him through our child minders and they had told us that he enjoyed boating, so we had decided to invite him along as a gesture of thanks. At this point we had no idea how valuable he was to become that day and how much we would learn from him in a few short hours.

We arrived at the marina at about ten in the morning and made short work of dispensing with the last of the paperwork before starting the engine and preparing to set off. The owner and the marina staff sniggered more than a little when I had to ask them which way we had to turn in order to get to Gayton and I suspect that they may have had a little bet as to how far we would get. Harold kept a straight face but I am sure that he was probably having similar thoughts – and as it transpired the one who had chosen the shortest distance would probably have won the bet had it not been for his help. As we left the marina I enquired whether Harold would like to have a go at steering the boat and he thanked me and said that he would.

As he took the helm it was immediately obvious that I had seriously underestimated his abilities. This was due entirely to the fact that no-one had told me that he had been a working boatman during the last of the commercial carrying days. As we approached the bottom of the Braunston flight he asked if I would mind if he made a few suggestions during the day to help us get to our destination more quickly and easily, and I agreed that this would be a good idea. Before I knew what was happening he was giving instructions to all of us, and Pam and Iain were sent off to "set ahead", a term I had never heard before. It proved to be one of many expressions that I would learn that day, and the first of many "little bits of advice" he was to give us which would help us considerably in our boating over the years. In fact I believe that I learned more in one day working with that old boatman than I had learned in about ten years previously.

We cleared the flight in what seemed to be record time and as we approached the entrance to the tunnel I turned on the tunnel light. No illumination! At this point I suppressed the urge to give in to the feelings of panic as I took the inspection lamp I had brought with me and headed into the boat to connect it via the cigarette lighter socket situated in the cabin. As I turned it on to light the way ahead all the lights in the boat went out as the fuse blew. By this time we were entering the tunnel and I expected Harold to stop and reverse out. As before, I had seriously underestimated him. With the attitude of an old boater he had decided that we were going to get to our destination no matter what and he proceeded to "push on" into the tunnel.

By this time I had found a small rechargeable torch, and under Harold's instruction I was sitting in the front deck area shining it into the gloomy darkness. I began to think that he had taken leave of his senses as we hurtled on through the pitch blackness and I wondered how he could possibly see the way ahead, because I certainly couldn't. To add to the confusion he would sound the horn every now and then and it wasn't until Pam made her way through the boat, sat beside me and informed me that the torch and horn were to warn other boats that we were there that I realised how remarkable he was, steering the boat in total darkness, through a tunnel known to have a kink in the middle, with no light. After a while my eyes became used to the darkness and I could just make out the sides of the tunnel illuminated by the dim little torch and I assume that Harold was steering the boat with just those little points of reference. I don't remember us touching the sides at all.

Half an hour later we emerged into the bright sunshine once more and before long were passing Norton Junction, where the Leicester line wandered off to our left, and approaching the top of the Buckby flight. As before, Iain and Pam were despatched to set the locks in front while I worked the boat through the locks. We reached the bottom in a little over forty minutes, a time I was very pleased with, although Harold thought that we had taken far too long. As we started on the last leg of our journey Pam went into the boat to make a pot of tea and I took the helm for the last few miles, feeling more than a little self conscious under Harold's watchful eye. Although he was invited inside the boat to eat his lunch he declined, explaining that he did not know us well enough to enter our boat. It was, in fact, several years and many visits before he would join us inside the cabin for a cuppa and a sandwich.

Iain had recently got himself a part time job at the chip shop in Cosgrove caravan park and was due to go to work that evening. In order to get him to work we had enlisted the services of my daughter Sarah, who had recently passed her driving test and had agreed to pick him up from a suitable point along our route, but unfortunately I had no idea where we were or how to get to us by road, and we were beginning to worry that he might not get there at all. Harold to the rescue once more. Although he didn't drive, he knew exactly where we were and also how to get to us by road, directing Sarah to the Narrowboat Inn near Weedon a couple of miles ahead. Such was his knowledge of the distances on the canals that he calculated that she should arrive there at about the same time that we would and that is exactly how it worked out. As we passed through the bridge hole just before the pub, Sarah's car turned into the car park and Iain hopped off and made his way across to her. We continued on our way to our final destination, arriving at our moorings just in time for sandwiches and a cup of tea before I drove Harold home.

We have done a lot of boating in the years since then but we will never forget that first journey on our first boat, or the old boater who was to become a very good friend, whose advice, freely given, would never be ignored. It was with some satisfaction that I pondered on the return journey from our little boat that she was, at last, truly ours.

Chapter 6

The Lift Bridge

By Geoff

There's a lift bridge, down the Oxford Canal. Well, to be truthful, that cut's littered with the dratted things, but there's one in particular, at a place called Thrupp – if you've boated that way, you'll know the one I mean. It leads into a Waterways maintenance yard, over the canal from the village, just past a right-angle turn if you're coming south from Banbury, so you can't see it until you get pretty close. A bit before the turn, there's an old bridge narrows, which gives you a handy place for someone to get off and run ahead to set the bridge.

It was a damp drizzly sort of Sunday, and we'd got thirty-odd tons on the pair – I was riding with Captain on the motor, and our mate was on the butty with his missus. You can guess who got elected to jump off and get the bridge.

I set off at a trot down the towpath, round the bend and up to the bridge – it's far enough for you to get a hundred yards or so in front if you hurry yourself. The bridge is one of those, typical Oxford style, with balance beams which stick up in the air at an angle when the bridge is down, and there was a chain dangling for you to get hold of and pull it down to open the bridge. I reached up, grabbed the chain, and heaved. The only result of this was that I found my feet waving in mid-air. I tried again, with the same result, all the time aware of the rattling of the old Lister getting closer and closer.

In a state of mild panic, I tried a third time – now, my feet were at least a foot off the ground, and still the b****y bridge wouldn't budge. Problem was, you see, Waterways had in their wisdom rebuilt it a bit before. Always used to be a wooden bridge, but now they'd replaced it with a steel one, which would have been all right except that they'd given it a wooden deck. In such wet weather, wood absorbs water and gets heavier, but steel doesn't, so by the time I got there the deck was about two hundredweight heavier than the balance beams. And I'm not exactly a heavyweight...

Next thing I know, the motor comes clattering around the turn, Captain happily expecting the bridge to be open for him.

Halfway around, he sees it isn't – hard astern with the engine, clouds of smoke from the exhaust, and... WALLOP!

Stempost hits the copings on the outside at forty-five degrees and the boat comes to an abrupt halt, the engine dying with a loud cough as it does so. So far so good – but the butty's still coming. Mate comes into the turn, sees the motor stuck against the bank, and aims to one side: Wallop! Hits the copings and parks the butty very neatly alongside the motor.

Yours truly is still dangling from the bridge. Mate runs down the top-planks on the butty and jumps off the fore-end to come and help, and between us we just about manage to get the bridge up. We sit, one on each balance beam, and turn to see what's happening with the boats. The sight that met our eyes will stay with me to the grave: Captain was a large and portly gentleman, usually of a very mild disposition, but at this moment in time he had obviously twigged what the cause of our problem was, and apportioned the blame with unerring accuracy. We sat there, open-mouthed, at the sight of him in grubby bib-and-brace overalls and a red check shirt, jumping up and down in barely-controlled fury, brandishing the cabin-shaft over his head as he called down all manner of calumny upon the heads of British Waterways in general, and upon whichever nationalized idiot had designed the new bridge in particular.

It took a few moments for him to recover his composure, upon which he shouted to us to 'leave that b****y bridge and come and 'elp!' It had been, I suppose, an inevitability that in the panic of trying to stop the boats without wreaking havoc upon the local countryside the towline had become inextricably entwined around the propeller. It took us a minute or so to unhook the line from the butty's T-stud and haul the motor around against the bank where we could get at things. And it took us, Captain, Mate and myself, the best part of half an hour, working in the damp and the drizzle, heaving and pulling with the cabin-shaft, winding the engine backwards and forwards, to retrieve the towline. When we did recover it, it had, fortunately, suffered no serious damage, merely winding itself very neatly around the propshaft.

At this point Mate's missus proved both her worth and her perspicacity. As we congratulated ourselves and set about carefully examining the rope to make sure it had ended up with no devilishly-concealed weaknesses that might cause it to snap at some embarrassing moment, she appeared from the butty cabin with four mugs of hot soup and four crusty rolls, warmed in the range's oven. Equanimity was soon restored, and, reassured about the condition of the towline, Captain restarted the engine and picked up the tow while Mate and I once more did our gymnastic thing with the bridge. It took all our combined weight and strength to keep it up long enough for the pair to get underneath, but we were able at last to let it drop and, heaving a sigh of relief, jump back on the boats and continue on our interrupted way.

A few months later they replaced the bridge again. With a wooden one.

Chapter 7

The Sudden Downpour

By Mac

It was as we approached the bottom lock at Grindley Brook that we noticed the group of people gathered there. The propensity of windlasses suggested that we had, once again, stumbled across another group of holiday makers aboard a hired narrowboat, and this was confirmed as we got closer and saw the hire company's distinctive logo on the boat waiting to begin its ascent of the locks. After a few moments we pulled in behind them.

As I tied our boat behind theirs, Pam walked up to offer assistance with the lock. We have found, over the years, that boaters fall into two main groups – those who know what they are doing and those who do not. And we have also found that people on hire boats can often be experienced and competent, while crews on privately owned boats do not always have the same level of ability as their counterparts on hire boats. So while Pam was being very nice in offering help, she was also "getting a feel" for their level of competence. As it was to transpire, however, it was not to be their level of expertise that was to be tested that day...

Fortunately, at this time, I was blissfully unaware of the events which were shortly to unfold, and I was looking forward to working up the flight of locks. After all it was a nice sunny day and the locks on this flight would provide us with some different challenges, the last three being a staircase, where one lock leads directly into the next.

We had spent the last week making our way up the Llangollen, or Welsh, canal and had become almost used to the side weirs which accompany each lock. Although side weirs are not uncommon on canals, those on the Llangollen are far more fierce than those normally found, due mainly to the fact that this canal is fed by the river Dee at its summit and therefore the water has a natural flow more common on rivers. This can catch out the unwary or inexperienced boater, but it's not too much of a problem if care is taken, because they are easy to see as you approach the lock.

However, at Grindley Brook there is quite a tight turn between the bottom two locks and the approach to the bottom of the staircase. This, in itself, may not be a great threat, but add the weir, a bridge to restrict the view and a hire boat leaving the lock and things can quickly turn quite nasty.

To continue with our story: We had made our way through the first two locks; the hire boat in front of us made their way into the bottom of the staircase as the other hire boat came out, and I started to take our boat through the bridge to moor and wait my turn to start the ascent.

As I exited the bridge-hole the boat coming down was swept across by the force of the weir. He indicated, quite correctly, that I should pass him on the other side, which I did. But as we passed two things happened in swift succession:

Firstly our boat was hit by the force of the water from weir, which caused my bow to veer away from the towpath and, of course, the lock landing; and secondly I swiftly ran out of room to manoeuvre, as the lock was getting quickly closer. I had no option but to go astern as the hire boat passed me, which caused the wild swing which our boat had started to become completely uncontrollable.

The net result of the whole manoeuvre was that the front end was swept into the bank on the left and the rear end was firmly pushed into the bank on the right. The crew of the hire boat going up suddenly appeared and looked down at me expectantly, obviously eager to see how an experienced boater would extricate himself from such a predicament. Not wanting to disappoint them, I decided that the best course of action was to reverse the boat away from the weir, turn back deftly into midstream, and moor on the lock landing. No problem there then.

As per the plan, I put the boat into astern and started to back away from the weir. Unfortunately the flow was stronger than I had anticipated and the front end of the boat stayed glued to the opposite bank as I moved slowly downstream. After about fifty feet I realised that this was not going to work and decided to try to drive the back end off the side instead.

My audience watched, enthralled, as I slowly made my way forwards again, the fore-end pushing along the opposite side and rear end sliding noisily along the towpath, to end up exactly where I had started. Panicking more than a little now, desperation took over and I decided to reverse back again, then drive the back end, forcefully, off the bank.

Pam chose this moment to walk down and try to assist me. "Throw me the centre line" she said "and I will pull it across." This would obviously not work, I thought, so I told her to wait a moment and give me one last chance to drive off. She stood there patiently waiting for me to fail again as I selected ahead gear and opened the throttle fully. What happened next was totally unexpected by me and Pam, but possibly not by the large group of boaters now collected at the lock and watching my every move. The engine roared in a huge cloud of black smoke, the water churned from the propeller and, as the front of the boat dug into the mud, the back end started to inch away from the bank. I looked round at Pam, expecting a look of admiration, but saw instead a look of horror, as she saw what I had failed to notice.

The huge plume of churning water from the propeller had hit the bank and was being diverted skywards in a giant inverted waterfall, or should it be called a waterrise?

Now, as an eminent scientist, I think it might have been Sir Isaac Newton, once observed "what goes up must, surely, come down". The enormous volume of muddy canal water started to fall, and as Pam disappeared beneath the torrent I reflected on the fact that I was now probably in deeper water than I had ever been before. As is often the case there was good news and bad news at this point.

The good news was that the boat was free at last from its wedged position. The bad news was that my "little cherub" was more than a little damp, and as the sudden downpour ceased and a deadly silence fell over the gathered throng at the lock I realised that this was the proverbial calm before the storm.

I cannot put down on paper the words used by my darling wife as she noisily pointed out the obvious fact that I had made a serious error of judgement in soaking her, telling me, and all the people now cowering behind the lock gates, in no uncertain terms that she did not find it in the least amusing that, despite several unsuccessful attempts over the years to knock her into the canal, I had finally managed to get her wet by throwing the canal over her! As her windlass bounced along the towpath and she stomped off towards the lock I sheepishly tied the boat on the lock landing.

The rest of the journey up the flight was a frosty affair, Pam refusing to dry herself until we moored at the top. With every squelchy wet step that she took it became obvious that it would be some time before I would be forgiven.

Chapter 8

The Irish Bog-warbler

By Geoff

A Preliminary Study Paper from the Nesting and Egg Research Department, Ornithology Faculty, University of Stoke Bruerne.

Recent work by NERD has followed from the interesting reports in the local press and elsewhere of unidentified birds apparently nesting, inverted, beneath the arches of canal bridges in Northamptonshire. It might at first be assumed that these reports are frivolous in intent, but we can now confirm that this is not the case.

Our initial findings are that the birds concerned are a sub-species of the Irish Bog-Warbler (Dampichirpicus Hiberniensis). It is not known for how long breeding pairs of the Bog-Warbler, whose natural habitat is the wet peat-bogs of the Irish Republic, have been living in Central England; it is thought probable that the first pairs arrived during the early part of the twentieth century, possibly blown across the Irish Sea by Atlantic storms or more likely as a result of becoming caught up in the migratory streams of the Crested Shamrock-Catcher, to which the Bog-Warbler is closely related. Being a non-migratory species, the latter has no determinable sense of direction, and could wind up almost anywhere once left behind by its faster-flying relatives.

Over the course of their evolution, the Bog-Warbler has become ideally adapted to its life in the peat-bogs: Its bright green plumage and bedraggled appearance allow it to blend in with its backdrop of rain-swept bogland. But perhaps its most remarkable attribute is its unique egg-laying procedure. A serious hazard to the Bog-Warbler at nesting time would be the risk of the eggs becoming displaced from the nest, set among the reeds in the wettest areas of the bog, upon which they would inevitably sink without trace into the water – but the female Bog-Warbler has developed the ability to generate in her intestines an amount of volatile gas, which a diversion from the colon allows to be injected into the eggs as they are produced. The result is an egg of unusually low density, so that, should it be inadvertently kicked from the nest by either bird's notably clumsy landings, it will float and can thus be retrieved.

In leaving their native peat-bogs, the Bog-Warbler has lost its normal food-source, the purple flowering bog-weed. It is the seed-pods of this plant which give rise to the gases in the female's intestine. In its place, the Bog-Warblers of Central England have taken to feeding upon a number of varieties of beans, mostly feasting upon the domestic broad bean to the infuriation of many keen gardeners and allotment-holders, and taking particular delight in the discovery of any quantities of discarded baked beans, which will be defended to the death against any intruder attempting to join in the feast. But this change of diet has had an unfortunate effect upon the female Bog-Warbler's egg-laying.

A diet of beans has resulted in a degree of over-production of the volatile gases used to lighten the eggs, as well as a change in the composition of those gases. The eggs produced by such females are now lighter than air, which it may be realised causes them some difficulty when it comes to laying – indeed 'laying' seems to be a somehow inappropriate term. As each egg is produced, its natural tendency to rise into the air has to be overcome, the female bird attempting to catch it under her wings and push it gently down into the nest beneath her. Any eggs not thus trapped float off on any prevailing air currents to an unknown fate. As may be readily understood, this task becomes increasingly difficult with every egg produced as any movement can have the unfortunate effect of releasing those already laid – it is rare for more than two or three eggs to be successfully kept for incubation out of the normal clutch of eight to ten. One side effect of this is that the female is then unable to leave the nest at all until the eggs

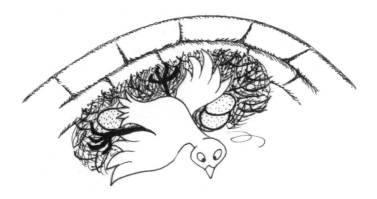

are hatched, relying solely upon her mate to bring her food, as to do so would result in the eggs escaping.

The recent reports mentioned above have led the research team to investigate, and our observations appear to confirm that some pairs of Bog-Warblers have adapted to this situation by learning to build their nests inverted beneath the arches of canal bridges. The obvious advantage of this is that the eggs can now be easily retained within the nest. However, such inverted nesting results in a new batch of problems for the unfortunate birds. Brooding requires a bird, either male or female, to be resident upon the nest for much of the time to provide the necessary warmth, and whilst the eggs may be lighter than air, the birds are not. So in order to roost, the bird must cling to the nest with its claws, hanging head-downwards – a most uncomfortable position, to say nothing of being extremely tiring, and thus these birds will be seen to change roles after a mere thirty to forty minutes.

This procedure also brings its own problems. The Bog-Warbler attempting to land upon an inverted nest has to perform an extremely gymnastic back-flip at the last moment before touching down, at the same time as grasping the structure of the nest – a highly complex manoeuvre, and one fraught with difficulty and indeed some danger. A failure to attach firmly to the nest will leave the unfortunate bird plummeting head-first into the canal beneath, after which the Bog-Warbler will be seen to clamber out onto the bank, shake itself vigorously, and rest for a minute or so before taking off to try again – being strictly vegetarian, the Bog-Warbler is not a natural diving bird. A secondary hazard can also arise if the nest is not sufficiently firmly attached to the brickwork of the bridge. An overly heavy landing can wrest the nest from its fixings, when the added weight of an adult bird brings the entire assemblage adrift and falling towards the water. Some quicker-thinking adult Bog-Warblers have been seen to instantly release the nest at this point, upon which the nest, buoyed up by the eggs within, promptly bobs up again against the bridge arch while the bird descends inevitably into the water. This altruistic reaction saves the eggs from a ducking (although it has to be admitted that it could simply be the result of shock). However, any further attempt to brood the eggs inevitably fails, as the nest cannot be re-attached to the brickwork.

Further observation and research will be required by NERD to bring more light upon this fascinating behaviour. Additional work will also be necessary upon the likely fate of any escaping eggs, with a particular emphasis upon determining if they are able to reach a sufficient altitude where, with their inflammable content, they may become a hazard to aviation.

I.M.A. Twitcher PhD Calcutta (failed), RSVP, BWB and bar

Chapter 9

The Meeting

By Mac

Pam was at work training lifeguards at a local swimming pool, our two children, Michelle, sixteen, and Iain, fifteen, were back at our house in the village of Yardley Gobion in Northamptonshire. I was aboard our boat, Calico, in the Marina which had recently opened next to the canal on the edge of the village. I was bored. It seemed wrong to waste the lovely summer afternoon so I decided to take the old girl out for a spin. Using my newly acquired radio communication device (mobile phone) I called the kids at the house to let them know that I would be at Cosgrove if they needed me, telling them that I would probably be back later in the evening. I am sure that this didn't deceive them but I hoped that it would deter them from inviting too many of their friends to go to the house and upset the neighbours. Another call to the swimming pool to leave a message for Pam and I was all set to make the short trip to Cosgrove.

About an hour later I moored up on the visitor moorings above the lock and went for a short walk to the old aqueduct and back with our dog Sox. On my return I fed the dog and checked the cupboards and fridge for something to eat and I was delighted to find among the tinned pies, bread, cheese and other sundry essential foodstuffs two large bottles of cider. I took my small meal and one of the bottles onto the front deck and settled down in the late afternoon sun to chill out until my darling wife returned from her labours.

It was about an hour and a couple of pints of the strong cider later that I noticed him. The little old man seemed to appear from nowhere, or had I just drifted for a moment into that daydream state that overtakes us from time to time? However it had happened, there he was. Small in stature, wiry with a grey beard, which made his thin face seem even thinner and wearing a baseball cap, he was within a few yards of the boat before I spotted him, almost as if he had sneaked up on me like a camouflaged soldier from an old war film. Taken aback, I said good evening to him and he stopped and turned his wrinkled old face to me, smiled broadly and wished me in turn a good evening.

There followed a bit of an awkward silence and I have often wondered whether this was a ploy by the "old gentleman" to put me off my guard. Before I knew what I was doing I found myself inviting him to sit down and offering him a drink. "Actually" he said "is that cider you're drinking, I'm quite partial to cider." If anyone else had made such a comment I would have been a bit miffed but it seemed completely natural for the old chap to treat me almost as if he had known me for years, so before I realised what was happening I was pouring him the first of several drinks that I was to dispense to him that day.

The afternoon turned into early evening and the light started to fade before he suddenly said that he should be on his way and stepped off the boat to walk off along the towpath, disappearing from sight in a matter of moments. At this point I noticed two things. Firstly I was very drunk and secondly there were two large empty cider bottles sitting on the deck of the boat! As I sat down unsteadily to try to collect my thoughts Pam appeared and cheerfully enquired how my afternoon had gone. Her demeanour changed abruptly as she spotted first the two empty bottles then my obviously inebriated state, jumping to the inevitable conclusion that I had consumed the whole quantity of alcohol from both bottles. I tried in vain to explain to her about the old man with the beard who had drunk most of it. "I suppose he was Santa Claus?" There was more than a hint of derision in her voice.

More than a year later we once again made our way to Cosgrove, under different circumstances. Our children had both finished school and decided to leave the nest and make their own

way in the world, so we sold our house to live a life of ease on the cut. Pam had already paid a visit to the small marina at Cosgrove to arrange a mooring for us, saying that the marina owner appeared to be a very nice chap and had told her to just pop down with our boat when we were ready and that he would "find us a spot". Upon our arrival we moored on the visitor moorings and Pam spoke to him again. We were told that our mooring was to be on the disused arm adjacent to the lock and that he would arrange for one of his staff to contact us "sometime over the weekend" to take us to our allocated mooring. In the meantime we were to feel free to have a look around.

We decided to take a look along the arm. As we crossed the lock and started to make our way along the towpath beside the old abandoned waterway I noticed that there seemed to be more than a few derelict fibreglass cruisers which seemed to have been abandoned by their owners. Combined with the overhanging tree branches and wild undergrowth along the edge of the towpath the panorama before us was rather less than idyllic. "What have you done to us this time?" I enquired of my wife, who seemed oblivious to the wilderness around us, to which she replied nonchalantly "It's not that bad. Anyway, we haven't seen it all yet". At this point I wasn't sure that I wanted to see any more but she was as enthusiastic as ever as she said "look – there's an old chap on that boat along there" and proceeded to stride off along the towpath to confront the said individual.

As we drew closer there seemed to be something unsettlingly familiar about the old man sitting on the deck of an equally old looking narrow boat. "Good afternoon" said my wife in greeting. "How do you do?" said the old man touching the peak of the baseball cap he was wearing, a greeting which should have seemed so old fashioned but somehow just seemed so charming. Suddenly the penny dropped as I recognised the thin face and grey beard of the wiry old man who had consumed most of my cider that sunny evening the previous year. "My name's Jack" he announced, "I'm very pleased to meet you".

After introducing ourselves we settled down to spend the rest of the afternoon with the old man who was to become a good friend to us, helping us to settle in to life "up the arm" and to appreciate the beauty in the seemingly desolate surroundings. On this occasion, as was to prove to be the case on many days, both sunny and less sunny, he was the perfect host and we drank more than a little alcohol provided by "Santa Claus".

Chapter 10

Getting It Wrong

By Geoff

We all get things wrong sometimes. But anyone who is a regular boater will tell you that things only ever go wrong when there's an audience. And when you're one of those who are supposed to know what they're doing, it only makes it all the more embarrassing.

I've told you already that I used to be captain of a trip boat – the Linda, which usually ran out of the old sand wharf at Cosgrove. Being an old (1912) Josher motor, it was also quite in place when, every summer, we went to Braunston for the annual historic boat show to run public trips there. The route we followed was the same as that of the historic boat parade – from the Stop House, by the old Iron Bridge which is now the entrance to the marina, down to the turn where the Grand Junction meets the Oxford Canal, round and back, and then into the marina itself, through and out of the second entrance under the 'Ladder Bridge'. No problem, you'd think. But the turn into the marina, under the Iron Bridge, is a bit sharp – far from impossible, but it is of course a point of honour to go round in one without any backing and filling. Most of the time, we'd manage it.

But once every year I'd get it wrong. Never on the dry run, with an empty boat and no spectators – oh no, it always happened with forty passengers on board, and upwards of four hundred onlookers on the bridge or the towpath. I'd come into the turn, heave over the 'ellum (it *was* a Josher) and wind up the engine. Much clattering of Lister, a nice rooster-tail of spray from the prop, and a resounding bang as the stem-post met the coping stones under the bridge. The impact would bounce the fore-end clear, and I'd vanish with a very red face into the marina. Free drinks all round to settle the passengers' nerves.

The other interesting bit of the route was the turn – for those of you who may not know it, Braunston Turn is a kind of three-way junction, with a little triangular island in the middle and two cast-iron bridges carrying the Oxford towpath over. To turn around, you go left around one side of the island and then reverse back up the other passing under each bridge in turn, then forward again to swing clear and go back the way you came. It helps if you have someone on the fore-end with a shaft to help with the reverse bit – most boats don't steer very well backwards.

Once I was doing shaft duty while a very competent employee steered – we went into the turn, pulled up neatly, and began to back around, yours truly duly shafting as required to keep the fore-end in line. With everything going smoothly, I raised the shaft clear...

I should tell you that Linda's shaft was about twenty feet long. And the towpath bridges had open cast-iron parapets. Yes, you've guessed. I narrowly missed spearing Granny with the top of the shaft as it passed neatly between the railings of the parapet, got caught there, and promptly snatched itself out of my hands as the boat continued on its way. I could have hung on, but I would have inevitably done for real what you might see in cartoons of incompetent gondoliers and ended up dangling from the wedged shaft. The cheers as we came forward again so that I could retrieve the shaft still echo in my memory.

Handling a pair of boats, motor and butty, is a whole different art from steering a single one. Loaded, you have to remember that there is another thirty tons of boat gaily following you along about eighty feet behind – getting around tight turns without dragging the butty into the inside bank requires taking the motor out really wide, as you might imagine. And don't forget that the butty has no brakes. Unloaded, you have the butty hung on tight

behind you, rather like an articulated lorry, on what are called cross-straps. No problem, either way. Usually. Locking through is more fun – it's a bit of a dark art running the motor in and loosing off the butty so that it glides up alongside you without the motor swinging sideways and blocking the butty's forward progress. And if you miss the breasting-string hanging from the shackle on the side of the butty, it goes steaming past you and hits the lock-gate with a nice loud bang, jangling the hanging-up plates and knocking the kettle off the range. Done right, it looks great – the motor slowing down, the butty gliding along until you drop the string over the motor's dolly and bring it to a gentle stop just up against the gates.

Coming out again can be fun, too. You have to run the motor forward, and, running empty, grab one of the cross-straps as the butty's fore-end goes past and get it over a dolly pretty quickly or you can literally miss the boat and wind up with the two travelling inexorably further and further apart. And if you've got the strap in your hand and fail to let go, you get a quick free bath into the bargain. I've seen seasoned boaters get that wrong, even a fellow I know who used to work the boats for real in the 1950s – and yes, I've done it too. Top lock at Stoke Bruerne, with the inevitable audience swelled by such canal notaries as David Blagrove, Mike Constable and Julia Cook, Y T came out of the lock on the back of the Nutfield and managed to miss the readied cross-straps on the Raymond. You feel such a twerp having to reverse back to pick up the butty in front of a grinning crowd.

Talking of Stoke Bruerne – they have a summer festival there every June, in aid of the Friends of the Museum. One time, we were there, all moored up above the top lock, where it gets a bit crowded with all the visiting boats. Many of them, ours included, are breasted side-by side, which leaves the gap down the middle a bit tight. A friend of mine, who to save his blushes I won't name, came up the locks with his pair and set off along the pound towards his allocated mooring. I don't know if he'd been enjoying the pleasures of the hops and malt along the way, but he decided to take fourteen feet of breasted boats through a gap which might have been thirteen feet wide...

It took us about half an hour to extricate them amid much ribaldry before he tried again, the boats singled out this time.

Perhaps the biggest embarrassment has to be running out of fuel. Yes, I've done that too! We had a private party on the Linda, going from Cosgrove to Great Linford and back, and just through Galleon Bridge in Old Wolverton the engine coughed and died. We shafted the boat to the bank and I tried to restart it, but the Lister wasn't having any of it. Now I will claim a bit of an excuse – there was a few inches of diesel showing on the dipstick. What I hadn't realised was that the pick-up which fed the engine was also a few inches above the bottom of the tank – sensible, really, as it stops you picking up silt from the bottom which might clog the injectors or ruin the pump. Free drinks all round again, a quick phone call, and Trevor from the Grand Junction Boat Company duly arrived with a big grin and a five-gallon drum of diesel.

So all you new-chum boaters, when you get things a bit wrong from time to time, console yourselves with the thought that even us professionals manage to s*d things up in spectacular fashion every now and then!

Chapter 11

Anchors Away

By Mac

A sunny summer's day on the north Oxford canal. We were making our way to the Thames and we were having a really nice time on one of the oldest and most beautiful of canals. Nothing was going to spoil our happy mood as we made our tranquil way on the last section towards Dukes Cut where we were to turn and travel the last short section to the great river

Now anyone who knows us will tell you that we have been prone to the odd scrape or two, the odd mishap on our boating journeys, and this day was about to follow a depressingly familiar pattern. When I say depressing some unkind friends of ours would say comical, or even hilarious. I will leave it up to you, the reader, to make up your own mind.

As I said, we had been fortunate so far on this journey and, as is often the case in these situations, I was to be the cause of my own undoing. For some time we had been following a pair of hotel boats as they locked down towards our final destination that day, but they were to take no blame for our impending disaster. The boats following us were also to be completely innocent of any responsibility.

As we waited our turn to go into the last lock before the turn and watched the hotel boats making the difficult job of working a pair of boats through a narrow lock look deceptively easy, a party off a hire boat behind us walked up to the lock and gazed in admiration at the sight of the boats being moved deftly through the lock and on their way. A sudden mad thought came to me as my wife filled the lock in order for us to proceed: I too would put on a bit of a show for the holidaymakers.

I walked up to the lock and quietly announced my master plan to my wife. I was going to strap in to the lock. She was not impressed and told me in no uncertain terms that she did not think that this was a good idea, but I was not to be deterred, having convinced myself that it would be a talking point for the people on the hire boat for years to come. Ominously, I was soon to be proved correct.

Strapping in is a trick used during the days of commercial boating to close the lock gate when travelling downhill into a lock and entails a rope attached to the stern being turned round a post on the end of the lock gate as the boat passes into the lock. The engine is taken out of gear and the momentum of the boat closes the gate, the rope then stops the boat before it hits the bottom gate. Very simple and effective when performed correctly.

I had made my preparations for our impending journey onto the river a little early, putting our anchor on its mounting on the rear of the boat. All went well as I came into the lock and deftly threw the line round the gate post. Unfortunately, as the line became taut it caught on the anchor and before I could react the anchor along with its bracket was pulled from the boat and dropped neatly into the lock entrance. The boat continued for a short distance then stopped abruptly as the lock gate jammed on the sunken steel obstruction.

So far so bad, but there was more to come on this hot sunny afternoon. Just as I thought that things could get no worse I made the basic mistake of acting before thinking. In my rush to extricate myself from my self imposed dilemma I decided to reverse the boat and retrieve the anchor, hopefully before anyone noticed my predicament. But my haste was to prove my undoing, for as I put the boat in gear the rope which I had expertly thrown round the lock gate post became slack, sank and was swiftly swallowed up by the spinning propeller.

Inevitably, several things now happened in very quick succession. The rope disappeared at an alarming speed until it jammed the propeller, causing it to stop abruptly and stall the engine; the lock gate was pulled sharply towards the back of the boat until it jammed on the sunken anchor; and the boat flew backwards, slamming into the jammed lock gate with a crash that was no doubt heard several miles away.

Things really could not get any worse, I thought. Oh yes they could! The crew from the hire boat were the first to arrive at the lock and it would be fair to say that they were seriously underwhelmed by my mastery of old boating techniques – as one of them said in an attempt at humour "you know, that would have been very impressive if it had worked".

My wife was less complimentary and I dare not write down her comments here. Suffice to say that she was not slow in letting me know exactly how she felt about the situation we were now in, explaining to the gathering throng of onlookers that I was regularly making an idiot of myself and that she had no idea why she put up with me at all.

By now there were boats approaching the bottom of the lock, adding to the numbers at the top, all waiting to pass through the inactive lock. As more people gathered my wife tirelessly explained to them what had happened, leaving them in no doubt as to who was responsible for the stoppage.

Fortunately with more people came more help and once I had cut the rope attached to the lock gate it didn't take too long for several of the more burly males to force the lock gate open, releasing the anchor, which was soon retrieved and dumped unceremoniously on the lock side. We pulled the boat into the lock, worked through and tied up below, allowing normal progress to resume. All that was left for me to do was to go into the weed hatch and spend about an hour cutting off the entangled rope from the propeller.

By the time I had finished the original onlookers had long gone, but several more had arrived and worked through, each new crew being treated to an explanation of my stupidity by my "ever loving"

while I beavered away in the weed hatch, trying desperately and unsuccessfully to hide my embarrassment. By the time we arrived at the first lock on the Thames even the lock keeper, from whom we had to purchase our visitor licence, took delight in letting me know that he was fully aware of the true extent of my boating expertise!

Chapter 12

The Door

By Mac

As I walked home along the towpath from my job in Wolverton on a sunny Saturday afternoon, I reflected upon how peaceful it was. I was looking forward to a relaxing afternoon at Cosgrove, with the possibility of a quiet pint with our friends on the moorings. Perhaps quiet is not the correct adjective to describe our drinking habits but I was looking forward to the prospect of an afternoon of socialising that would, inevitably, stretch through the evening and long into the night, with the probability of a flotilla of narrowboats making their way to the Navigation pub at Castlethorpe. These trips had become a bit of a tradition and we would often find ourselves tied several boats abreast along the moorings outside the pub. The trip back to the moorings, often late at night, was a sight to behold as most of the steerers would be rather the worse for wear and often verging on the noisy. In those days, however, no-one seemed to mind too much, probably because most of the local boaters were involved in the fun.

This Saturday afternoon was to be a little different, however. Geoffrey Lewis was the proprietor of the local trip boat business, the Linda Cruising Company, and owner and skipper of the narrowboat Elizabeth of Glamis. Geoffrey had become a good friend of mine and my wife's and, over the years since, we have had many adventures with him. He subsequently sold the business and we continued to work with the new owner for several years, but that is the stuff of other stories. On this day, Geoffrey had taken the boat down through the lock on a short trip across the Iron Trunk aqueduct, turning outside the Galleon pub in Old Wolverton, and was just leaving the lock on his return journey as I walked up the towpath. Although it was not unusual for the trip boat to attract some attention it was obvious that the scene manifesting itself before me was unusual for several reasons: Firstly, Geoffrey seemed more than a little agitated. Secondly, there were more people around the lock than I would normally have expected to see. The most unusual thing, however, was the fact that most of the people gathered there were boaters from the moorings, who would not normally take too much notice of the trip boat.

As I reached the lock, one of them explained to me the reason for the gathering and, if I had had any sense at all, I would have realised that things were soon going to become very interesting, and I would have headed straight for my own boat and a bite of lunch. It seemed that one of the side hatch doors had opened a little as the boat was in the lock on its outward journey and had caught on the lock side as the boat descended. The doors on Lizzie, as she is affectionately known, were fitted in such a way that they could be removed by simply lifting them off their hinges, and the open door had been so removed by a combination of friction against the lock side and a twenty ton boat being slowly lowered. The first indication that anything was wrong was the loud splash as the displaced steel door dropped into the water and disappeared from sight into the swirling muddy depths of the lock. Geoffrey had had no option but to continue with his trip, contemplating the probability that a costly new door would be the inevitable outcome of this small disaster. Which explained why he had seemed less than completely happy as he made his way back up through the lock and moored on the wharf above.

Being a sensible chap, it is a matter of opinion as to whether he would have thought that the next sequence of events was a good idea. But as he was busy at the time, tying up the boat and seeing his passengers off, and so was thankfully unaware of the plan suggested by one boater at the lock and quickly gathering support among the others. I should point out that most of the gathered throng had already started the afternoon in the usual fashion and were probably not at their intellectual best, but this did not deter them from making the decision to try to retrieve the door from the lock.

A plan was soon formed and the excitement grew rapidly as a small rowing boat was produced and launched into the wide-hole below the lock to allow a couple of the more intrepid members of the group to enter the lock with two powerful magnets in order to lift the door from its watery grave. At this point a small hiccup occurred. It seemed that, whilst they were all in favour of the plan in theory and despite the fact that their normal reticence was impaired by the amount of alcohol consumed, none of them seemed driven to actually board the bobbing little craft.

As the discussion continued I was handed a drink, then another, and all of a sudden it seemed obvious that, as Geoffrey was such a good friend of mine, I should be the first to show willing. I have often tried, without success, to remember whether it was my own idea or a suggestion by one of the more reluctant members of the group but I found myself being helped, by several inebriated colleagues, into the unstable little craft which would shortly carry me towards the rescue attempt.

My boarding was made even more perilous by the fact that someone chose this moment to empty the lock with the result that the little boat spun precariously in the swirling water as I struggled to keep my balance. By this time the whole endeavour had taken on a life of its own and anyone looking on could have been forgiven for thinking that a lifeboat was being launched to rescue some poor drowning wretched from a stormy sea! The hatch door, it seemed, had to be rescued no matter how dangerous the consequences, and soon another volunteer stepped unsteadily forward.

Had I not already been installed in the boat I would certainly not, under any circumstances, have entered it with the person who now lurched across the towpath towards me. For legal reasons I dare not mention his name, but anyone who was in the area at the time might conceivably recognise the person I am about to describe: He worked for a local building plant company and claimed to be Canadian; a very helpful sort of person, he was what used to be described as a disaster waiting to happen. That was when he was sober. When drunk the disaster had become almost inevitable. Still in his customary working overalls and rigger boots, he noisily made his faltering way to the boat and, before anyone could stop him, lurched aboard. My heart sank as the small craft almost turned turtle, and with a slurred "alright Mac" he handed me another beer, opening one for himself as well.

Before I could even attempt to extricate myself from my predicament I felt the boat surge forward. The boat sped away from the safety of the bank and I almost fell in as several eager boaters pulled it swiftly if unsteadily into the lock. My compatriot added to the confusion by toppling into me, and it was certainly only luck that prevented us both from departing unceremoniously overboard. As suddenly as it had sped forward, the little rescue craft stopped and, once again, we came perilously close to dropping into the watery depths. The assorted rabble on the lock side, consuming copious quantities of alcohol, encouraged us noisily as we spent the next half hour or so, between beers, plumbing the depths with our magnets.

Geoffrey watched hopefully, and several boats started to queue impatiently at each side if the lock. Under normal circumstances the bottleneck would almost certainly have resulted in a confrontation between the waiting boaters and those causing the delay, but on this occasion everyone seemed more interested in watching the fascinating goings-on. Or perhaps no-one was keen to argue with the ever growing throng of tipsy onlookers at the lock, who were becoming almost uncontrollable in their excitement.

Pulling the small rowing boat this way and that, shouting encouragement and even taking pictures, they seemed more than a little intimidating even to me, and they were my friends!

Suddenly my companion yelled "I think I've got it" and hopped about alarmingly threatening, yet again, to capsize us. As soon as he had calmed down sufficiently to allow me to regain my balance I dropped my own magnet in next to his and, sure enough, it attached itself to something obviously large and heavy. We waited for a short while, steadying ourselves as best we could while our ecstatic comrades on the lock side jostled to see what was happening, causing the little boat to lurch alarmingly backwards and forwards, threatening to dash it to pieces against the slimy brickwork.

Slowly we started to lift, and soon there was a loud cheer as the door appeared at the surface. We carefully eased it into the boat, and within a few moments we were pulled from the lock. With the retrieved door safe on the bank we were hailed as heroes, and the canal was allowed to settle back to its normal routine.

As I stood among the crowd and Geoffrey thanked us both for the rescue of his expensive piece of equipment, I turned to my fellow rescuer and commented on the fact that it was fortuitous that we had not both taken a bath in the canal.

"A real good job" he replied "I can't swim." At this point the assembled group fell about laughing uncontrollably. Once everyone had recovered, we did the first sensible thing we had all done since the beginning of the adventure. We went to the pub.

Drinks on Geoffrey.

Chapter 13

Stemmed Up

By Geoff

I've mentioned my trip-boating days, with the old Linda. That old lady was unusually deep in the water, even for an ex-working boat – she had been built in 1912, and originally intended to have a steam engine although she in fact came off the dock with the first Bolinder ever fitted by Fellows, Morton & Clayton to one of their boats. The steamers always swung a huge propeller, three feet in diameter – and that meant that the Linda drew three feet three inches at the rudder, even standing still. More like three feet eight when she was going along.

We used to do a regular day of trips for Northampton Borough Council, a couple of times a year, from Gayton Junction near Blisworth down the arm to Northampton, and it must have been around 1997 or '98, when we set off once more on this trip. Near the Northampton ring road, they'd been laying in the services for a new housing estate, which had entailed burrowing under the canal for a new sewer, using one of those astonishing boring machines like they used for the channel tunnel – but a bit smaller, of course. Anyway, there we were, trundling gaily along, heading for Hardingstone Lock, the ring road bridge coming up, when the boat came to a sudden stop, in the middle of the channel, for no apparent reason.

We'd obviously run up on something. I tried going astern, to back of off whatever it was – no good. More revs – still stuck fast. The crew, an old friend by the name of Howard, had twigged that something was wrong. He climbed out onto the fore-end and shafted the bow across to one side while I tried going hard forwards, tiller hard over, trying to get off sideways. That didn't work either. Backwards and forwards we tried for while, with the passengers getting ever more impatient with our lack of progress. A pause for thought, and free drinks all round to keep them quiet.

'If we got everyone to go to the front of the boat...' Howard suggested.

These old working boats tend to sit very nose-high, so that the bottom slopes down from front to back – and we were stuck near the stern, so his idea had merit. But I wasn't keen on causing even more unrest among the milling throng down below. However, I let him persuade me, if only because the only alternative seemed to be to spend the rest of the day where we were.

His diplomatic skills proved far superior to my own – in fact, our forty passengers not only took it on good part but actually seemed to think it was a great joke as they all huddled together in very intimate fashion in the fore-part of the cabin. And it did the trick – the stern came up a few inches, which might give you some idea of the girth of some of the passengers, and we floated gently over the obstruction and on our way. And applying the same trick as we approached the spot on the return trip got us over again without delay, to the further amusement of all except me! It turned out that the contractor's wonderful drilling machine had pushed the bottom of the canal up a bit as it cut through underneath – British Waterways dredged it out again when I told them about it. Bless 'em.

'Stemmed up' is the old boatman's expression for getting stuck. And I have yet to meet a boater of any generation who hasn't managed it at some time or another! Even the most experienced can get caught out from time to time, even if the cause can be somewhat abstruse – I once spent four happy hours in the drizzle in a cutting near Olton, in Birmingham, trying to get an empty motor boat off of some kind of lump on the bottom of the canal. We gave the local population some amusement with our efforts, even roping a few in, literally, getting them to heave on lines in an attempt to pull us free. One couple, walking their dog, stopped to

help, but we let them carry on after our efforts proved futile. But they were back a few minutes later – their black Labrador had been so fascinated by what was going on that it had decided staying to watch was going to be more fun than finishing its walk, and only went with them after some persuasion and the attaching of its lead.

We did eventually get off, with the aid of British Waterways and a turfor winch. When they got the lump out, it proved to be – a safe! From where, we never did find out. Nor what had happened to the contents...

On another occasion, I was steering the motor of an empty pair southwards on the Grand Union. Through Blisworth village and into the cutting leading to the north end of the tunnel. Just approaching the black hole, another boat came out, and I held over to keep out of his way – a big mistake! There's a feeder that runs down the side of the cutting just there, and inevitably it deposits a kind of sand bar on the bottom where the water flows in. And I found it. Travelling quite fast, ready for the run through the tunnel, the stern was about four inches out of the water by the time we ground to a halt. Another couple of happy hours, although thankfully it wasn't raining this time – and it took all the ingenuity of the captain, a far more experienced boater than I was, to finally get us off.

I remember a boating holiday, when I was with a group of friends on two boats. We had gone up the northern Oxford Canal, towards Coventry, which in those days was pretty shallow in places. I was steering the leading boat, and, hearing a shout, looked back to see that the other steerer's hat had blown off in the breeze. He'd gone astern, trying to retrieve it, and got stuck when they drifted into the shallow water on the offside. This struck me as funny, and I had a big grin as I put our boat astern to go and help.

The grin didn't last long. Next thing I knew I was on the mud too, stuck fast. Luckily it was bright sunny day, and we had a supply of beer on board, which helped enormously with both our mood and our efforts to get moving again. Which we did – eventually.

And we even got his hat back, too.

Chapter 14

Traditional Boating

By Mac

It has been said that if you want the answer to any question then you should spend an evening in the Boat Inn at Stoke Bruerne and you will be duly enlightened. I had always been sceptical of this, but some years ago now my wife and I were relaxing with some friends and partaking of some refreshment when we were treated to an explanation of a solution to an age old boating problem. Among the gathered throng in the bar were two chaps talking quite loudly about traditional boats and boating methods. Now I know what you are thinking, but rest assured the following tale does not relate to the two most popular subjects of boating discussion (engines and toilets) but to a far more serious matter.

After the two men had exhausted the usual topics of traditional boating; types of load, old boaters names, the jam 'ole run etc. they turned their attention to a topic which caught our attention immediately. Water cans, or as they referred to them, Buckby cans.

It seems that they had given these innocuous items some considerable thought and after whanging on for some time about the different shapes, sizes and styles of decoration they came to an age old boating problem. My wife in particular was intrigued by the sudden strange turn in the conversation as one guy said

"I have a foolproof way of stopping my can blowing off the cabin roof in the wind". Now I have to say that my first thought was that I had misheard him but I was soon reassured that this was not the case when his friend replied:

"So have I, I put a brick in mine".

At this point my wife started to smile broadly and the thought passed through my mind that at last I truly had heard everything, but there was to be so much more! We waited with bated breath for the conversation to continue, and we were not to be disappointed as the first guy, not to be outdone by his companion, spoke more words of wisdom. "You have to be really careful that the brick doesn't scratch the inside of the can, that's why I always wrap my brick in bubble wrap".

At this point their attention was diverted from the discussion by the strange sight of my wife almost crying with laughter and in imminent danger of falling off her chair.

"What's so funny?" demanded one of the guys.

"You and your water cans" she replied through the tears now running down her cheeks.

"I don't see anything funny" says the man in indignation.

"You would if you were sitting here listening to yourselves" she said, to which he retorted indignantly

"I suppose you have a better way of keeping a can on the cabin roof?"

"Of course" she said "we use the traditional method of filling our can with water". At this point the guy became extremely agitated and proclaimed loudly:

"How do you stop it going rusty then?" When she explained to him that water cans are made of galvanized metal in order to prevent this happening he became almost incoherent in his indignation, and he and his friend left the pub amidst raucous laughter and headed back to their boats.

Now you may think, as I did, that this would be the end of my little tale, but there was to be one final twist. As we made our rather drunken way back to our own boat we passed one of the "water can" men standing in the hatch of his highly polished boat with its traditional engine sparkling in its impeccably clean engine hole and its brass gleaming in the moonlight. As we passed him the man made a rather derogatory comment to us about the evening's proceedings and made the observation that in his opinion we knew nothing about traditional boating. As he ranted on my wife seemed to be taking rather a big interest in his cratch area. At last he became quiet and after a moment's silence my wife said:

"Can I ask you a question about your traditional boat?"

"Fire away" he replied smugly.

"Where do you put the twenty tons of coal?" she asked innocently.

Chapter 15

A Few Useful Tips
or
12 Ways to Kill Yourself
with a Narrowboat

By Geoff

There was a time when all the boats on the canal were crewed by people who were doing it for a living; and virtually all of them had been born and brought up on the boats. Safe and efficient boating was not just second nature to them, it was their whole way of life. But now, nearly all the boats about are manned by newcomers, pleasure-boaters who maybe get out on the cut once or twice a year – and I include myself in that number! I've been very lucky to have been boating with those who once did it as a living, and to have been allowed to play with old working boats, both empty and loaded, but I'm still an amateur, a Johnny-come-lately, like everyone else.

But some of the practices that I see around the cut today do make me shake my head and wonder at the IQ of some of today's boaters. Let me give you a few examples:

Steering traditional or semi-trad boats: A trad boat has a cabin that extends almost to the stern end – the tiller reaches over the top of the cabin, with just a very short rounded counter deck behind; a semi-trad looks the same, but is kind of cut away inside so that the stern cabin is just an open shell. Both types should be steered from <u>inside</u> the profile of the cabin, so that the steerer is in front of the tiller – but how often do you see people steering them, stood outside, balanced precariously on the little counter deck? They look pretty stupid, as you may have observed – more

importantly, this is an excellent way of committing hara-kiri. Meet an obstruction, slam the gear lever into reverse, and the prop-wash snatches the tiller out of your hand as the rudder swings to one side. One way, and you just lose hold of it – the other, and you're trying to swim away from the churning blades of the prop. Instant mincemeat.

All joking aside, I have spoken to the fire crew who had the task of removing a school-teacher from the propeller of a hired boat where just that had happened. In front of a group of kids. Not nice.

Knitting on the tiller-pin: Most boats' tillers are retained by a little pin, with an ornamental knob on the top. The knob is just that –

ornamental. It isn't for hanging the stern mooring line over when you're under way. You can, of course – but it does look very girlie, doesn't it? And the result is a length of rope dangling from tiller to dolly, beautifully placed to trip you up if for any reason you take a step backwards on the stern of the boat. Once again, a graceful swan-dive places you within a couple of feet of a spinning propeller.

I've lost count of the number of times that's happened in recent years – another very messy way of going to meet your maker. Take the rope off the dolly, coil it up, and put it on the cabin roof where it's to hand if you need it, but where it can't do anyone any harm!

Talking of ropes: Bits of rope on a boat are there for a purpose. When they're not in use, keep them where you can reach them if you need them, neatly coiled so that they come to hand. Not tangled into a useless mass so you spend five minutes unravelling them as the boat drifts over the weir, nor beautifully turned into a perfect flat, round disc so that you can't find the end when you need it, and in the middle of the roof where it's nicely out of reach anyway.

The most useful rope on any boat is a centre line, attached around the mid-point and kept where the steerer can reach the other end. With it, <u>one person</u> can control the boat by stepping off onto the bank with it in hand. But only if he can reach it.

And when you moor up, tie the boat tightly, not with about six feet of free movement! Canals generally don't go up and down – the tides don't affect the Grand Union much, and the level is controlled by weirs and pumping, so unless you're in a short pound between locks – where you shouldn't moor anyway – you've no need for slack in the ropes. And keeping them tight means that if someone goes by a bit too fast, you don't get your tea in your lap, because the boat doesn't move!

And remember, if you're using mooring pins, angle them away from the boat, and hammer them well in, so you don't wake up in the morning and find yourself in a different place from where you went to sleep.

Another thing that gives me the jitters is to see a boat, usually one of the charity-run boats that takes groups if kids out from inner-city areas for 'a bit of countryside', with about twelve youngsters sitting or standing on the roof.

Now I'm not knocking what these charities do, in fact I'm all for it, but so often the steerers don't seem to see the danger of this – how the blazes can they see where they're going, for a start?

Not only that, but it does it make the boat unstable, and then, one slip, and you're trying to retrieve a soggy teenager from the cut. In a lock, and that could result in an inquest. And before you say that surely no-one would let kids run around on the roof of a boat in a lock...

Another thing they'll do if you don't watch them is sit on the fore-deck. No danger in that – unless they've left a leg or two dangling over the side, across the guards... A moment's inattention, an approaching boat or a bridge-hole, and you've got an instant candidate for the part of Long John Silver in the next production of Treasure Island. Even at four miles an hour, your shinbone won't survive the impact, trust me.

If you've got kids on a narrowboat, another ongoing debate concerns life-jackets. And now I'm going to upset a lot of people! I don't like them. A life-jacket can all too easily give a youngster the 'can't-happen-to-me' syndrome we see in sales reps on the motorway with their new BMWs, with the traction control and anti-skid and anti-lock brakes. They'll take too many chances. I'd rather a kid with no life-jacket and a healthy awareness of danger! And most life-jackets add to the bulk of the clothing, which can very easily throw them off-balance, for example when crossing lock-gates – and yes I want to see youngsters taking part in boating, not super-glued into the foredeck at all times. Most of the canals are quite shallow, so an inadvertent ducking is not difficult to retrieve – the dangers come from the propeller, or in locks when the paddles are running, and in either of those situations a life-jacket isn't going to be much help. And before anyone says it – my twelve-year-old stepson comes with us on the working boats, and he's the most precious thing in my life. By a long way.

While we're on the subject of locks: Once you've worked out which end of the windlass is which, you proudly put it on the spindle and wind up the paddle – now, don't leave it there! If the catch slips, your windlass can achieve something approaching mach one as it flies off the spindle. Enough to clear the roof of the lock-cottage, break a window, or your arm. And spending the rest of your boating holiday in plaster does take a lot of the fun out of it.

And every time you come to a lock – look at the other end of it! Make sure the gates are closed, and the paddles down, before you try to fill or empty it, or you can be standing there for a long time. And do look to see if anyone's coming the other way – it saves wasting water, not to mention a severe case of apoplexy, if you don't turn a lock around in front of an approaching boat which might have used it the way it was.

When you're going uphill in the locks, you'll see those nice little notices telling you not to open the gate paddles until the lock is half-full – take heed of them! This is one place where our practice with the old working boats differs from what I'm advising you to do – with a working pair, we leave the motor in forward gear so that the stem-post is right up against the top gates. That way, you can pull all the paddles straight away, and the water from the gate paddles goes down each side of the boats. But with a modern boat, usually much shorter than ours, you tend to sit back from the gates; and now, if you pull the gate paddles too soon, you can easily get a lovely jet of water, about twelve inches by eight, straight in through the front doors. Does the carpets no end of good – and if you don't notice in time, British Waterways will be sending you a nice bill for draining the lock and pumping your boat out.

If you really want to sink your boat in a lock, while going downhill, a good way of doing it is to have your front fender tightly chained into place. All you need to do then is empty the lock while allowing the boat to drift forward – the fender hangs up on the bottom gate, the stern end goes under water, and hey

presto! Out with the pumps again. A loose fender, or a split link in the chain, and that will give before the boat goes under.

Well, I hope the foregoing has been helpful – I've given you a number of ways of disposing of unwanted crew members, or collecting the insurance on your boat. You can't say you haven't been warned!

Chapter 16

The Brady Bunch

By Mac

Pulling up at the bottom of the Buckby flight near Weedon on the Grand Union Canal, we anticipated spending the next hour or so working up the flight. As we walked up to set the first lock we noticed another boat approaching from below, and hoped that they would be joining us on our journey through the big Grand Union locks. As we emptied the lock and awaited the arrival of the craft below we noticed that they had a rather large crew, six in all, and thought that it might be a hire boat. Now I would like to say that we have no problem working with people on hire boats, in fact we quite enjoy doing so most of the time. After all they are usually very keen and there is always the chance that they have had a few holidays in the past, so may not be as inexperienced as some people might expect. In any case their enthusiasm often outweighs any lack of knowledge. The crew now approaching the lock landing, however, were to prove a different breed altogether and, although we were not aware of it at the time, we were about to embark on a journey through the locks which we would never to forget!

The first clue to the impending mayhem presented itself as they sped along the moorings leading to the lock landing at a pace which would have left Stirling Moss wondering how to keep up.

We watched in horror as they sped ever closer to our moored boat, the impending collision seeming inevitable. Suddenly the speeding vessel disappeared in a huge cloud of black smoke as the helmsman selected astern gear and attempted to avert disaster. For a few seconds longer we were unsure whether he had been successful or not as the engine screamed from within the mist and the wave of water being sucked through the whirling propeller washed along the canal rattling the boats moored at the marina wharf opposite. As the noise abated and the cloud settled we saw the craft stationary a foot or so behind our own, the crew leaping ashore with enough rope to tie a fleet of ships and enough windlasses to supply a small chandlery. For the next few minutes, as the lock emptied, the young crew, under the direction of their much older "skipper", proceeded to tie their vessel securely to the bank using every inch of their considerable stock of rope, and several seafaring knots, some of which I recognised and some which I had never seen before.

Eventually the lock was ready and I walked down to our boat. As I approached them "skipper" asked me if I was going up the locks. "No" I thought "I just thought I'd set the lock for fun" as I said "yes, are you?"

"Yes" he replied, then rather ominously "perhaps we can share?" Now after the recent display of seamanship demonstrated by him and his crew I didn't feel much like taking the chance but my soft nature got the better of me as I agreed, after all it couldn't be that bad could it? Wrong again! As I was nearer the lock I went in first and held our boat to the side as we waited for the plethora of knots to be untied. This task performed, the crew all made their way to the lock, each carrying a windlass, and the captain prepared to set off from his mooring. He settled himself at the tiller and set off for the lock as if all the hounds of hell were chasing him!

For a few moments he disappeared in another cloud of black smoke as the poor engine screamed, the water behind was turned into a raging plume and several yards of the towpath disappeared beneath the wave, to be turned into a muddy swamp.

I thought that my days were over as the speeding craft hurtled towards me. As he entered the lock tail he once again selected astern and attempted to slow down before tearing into the lock. He might have been successful if there had not been a large obstacle in his path, namely our boat. With a resounding crunch he hit it, bouncing across the into the lock wall, stopping abruptly before driving alongside me.

"Sorry about that" he said as he came to a final stop "but it is a contact sport!" Normally I would have lost my temper at this point but I was just happy to still be alive, and he had *almost* stopped his vessel before hitting ours, so the impact wasn't as serious as it had sounded. Now I found myself speechless as I watched him direct his crew, standing eagerly along the lock side. Once more all the ropes were deployed and various different knots ensured that the craft was secured against all possibility of movement, as if we were to expect some freak tropical storm, and the entire crew disappeared from my view, running eagerly towards the top gates, windlasses at the ready.

At this point Pam took over on the lock side bringing their headlong rush to an abrupt halt with a commanding:

"STOP!"

As she explained to me later, they did as they were told with a mixture of alarm and confusion, the first sensible thing they had done so far. Now anyone who knows my "beloved" will tell you that she is not one to be messed about with and she has some very simple rules which she applies around locks.

Firstly only one person, usually her, is in charge, secondly nothing is done without first checking with the helmsman and finally, and most importantly, no running on the lock side. It was once pointed out to her by an ill advised individual that if the boat were to get caught on the sill or lock gate then it might be necessary to run in order to remedy the situation. Her reply was instant and caustic: "If you abide by the first two rules and keep an eye on the boat it should never happen"

She then proceeded to relieve them of all but one of the windlasses, explaining that they would only require one for this lock, as she would be operating one side while one of them could do the other. She allowed two more windlasses to be taken to set the next lock ahead, but sent the rest back to be deposited with their captain. With the excess hardware returned to he bemused skipper of their vessel the crew went back, at walking pace, to the top gates, to await further instructions from my "little cherub"

As the lock filled "skipper" turned to me and said "You'll have to excuse my crew, they're not very experienced and I'm still trying to get them trained up". My first thought was to advise him to go and get some instruction of his own but instead I asked him how long he had been boating, and was amazed when he said "about twelve years". After further questioning, however, he told me that he had been in a time share during these years, owning a two week share. Doing the maths in my head I calculated that this amounted to a little short of six months actual boating, but I was still staggered that so far he had not seriously injured anyone

– or at least I presumed he hadn't. He went on to tell me with great pride that his present crew were his grandchildren and their friends and that they were following in their own parent's footsteps, a crew he had also trained. I had a sudden vision of several generations of his family roaring around the canal system in the same fashion as him.

With great effort I put this thought from my mind as the lock filled and the gates opened. As the next lock was ready I suggested that we pootle up together. Another mistake! "Skipper" seemed to have only one way to move his boat, i.e. very quickly, and surged out of the lock at full speed, leaving me bobbing in his wake! As the waters settled I set of at a more leisurely pace and followed him across the short pound to the next lock as Pam and Co closed the gates behind us. Once again he shot in to the lock and screeched to a halt a few yards from disaster, and once again the vessel was secured to the lock side by several lengths of rope, looking as if it had become entangled in some giant cobweb.

At this point I started to see the funny side of our little adventure and decided that, as I was to be unable to curb his enthusiasm for violent operation of his poor vessel, I would let him go ahead at each lock and wait for him to sort himself out before following.

Having adopted this approach we worked up the next few locks in almost total chaos and I found myself actually enjoying the sight of "skipper" tearing into the locks and the inevitable rope throwing and tying up, the operation seeming to become more comical at each lock. By the time we were about halfway up I was actually laughing as a fresh disaster seemed to occur at each lock. At one he tried to charge in through one gate and almost knocked a crew member off her feet as he "clipped" the opening gate at about mach 2; at another he managed to miss the entrance completely, even though both gates were open, and careered into the lock bouncing from wall to wall!

With sides almost splitting I watched as he approached another lock with his usual gusto and started to throw up the ropes. As he threw the last one I noticed that Pam was waiting to catch it, and that he had completely missed the lock side, the rope instead travelling vertically upwards about three feet out from the side. Pam watched as the rope flew up and then dropped neatly into the water next to the boat. "Skipper" seemed to go into panic mode as he frantically coiled the rope and sent it flying back up towards my other half. She was obviously not too pleased at

being attacked by a wet rope but caught it anyway and started to pull it up. Very soon she was looking at the eye in the end of the rope which should have been over the dolly on the boat. She looked over at "skipper" and asked politely:

'Shouldn't there be something attached to the end of this?'

Unfortunately, in his haste to deploy this essential part of his safety equipment, "skipper" had dislodged the other end of the rope from the dolly on the stern of the boat. Pam started to lower one end back down to him in order that he could make his vessel fast once more, but he seemed to be in a real panic as all this went on and I had to hold onto the cabin side as I became weak with laughter and my legs threatened to give way beneath me.

I calmed myself down before entering the lock and as it filled I called Pam over and told her that I was feeling unwell and would not be able to proceed any further up the locks until I could have a lie down. She looked at me with a mixture of worry and bewilderment – after all I had seemed to be enjoying myself. It wasn't until "skipper" and crew had gone that I could explain that the reason I couldn't carry on was that I didn't think my heart could take the strain of such endless amusement!

Chapter 17

What a Waste

By Mac

Pam had driven down to my mother's house in Harefield and brought her back to spend the weekend with us. Like many elderly people she had stopped venturing out as often as she had when she had been younger, and after my father's death a few years earlier she had become even more reclusive. So we were really pleased that she had decided to accept our invitation to spend a few days with us and it was with great excitement that we helped her aboard our little boat, Calico, in the marina. Before settling herself in her usual position on the front deck she asked to use the toilet, so I took her into the boat and explained how the toilet worked. It was a cassette unit with an electric flush and I explained that it only required the button to be held down for a few moments in order to flush it. She nodded politely and said that she understood so I left her to use the apparatus in peace while I started the engine and prepared to get under way.

A few minutes later Pam called me back into the boat to tell me that my mother was having a little trouble with the toilet. When I went to investigate I found that there was no water being pumped when the flush was operated despite the pump whirring noisily. Upon checking a little deeper I found that the top tank containing the flushing water was empty and I decided that I had obviously forgotten to top it up correctly after emptying the cassette when we had returned from our previous trip. I filled it and pressed the knob to pump some water into the bowl. When I pulled the lever to empty it into the bottom tank I was more than a little surprised to see that it was full, as I was sure that I remembered emptying it the previous weekend. Despite this I decided that I must have just forgotten so I changed the cassette for the spare and continued to untie the ropes, and we set off for Cosgrove where we would stop for lunch and I could empty the full cassette.

The journey took us about an hour and we soon pulled up alongside the water point, and as the water tank filled I took the cassette to empty it. As I walked past the boat on my way back I could hear what I thought was the water pump whirring and was most surprised to see Pam standing on the front deck, as I had hoped that she must be filling the kettle for a cup of tea.

"No" she said "I'm just waiting to use the toilet, your mum's in there". As I stepped into the boat I could still hear the pump and realised that it wasn't the water pump but the toilet flush that I could hear. I called to my mother and the pump stopped as she reappeared. I walked through to the toilet and checked it. I was astonished to find that the top tank was, once again, empty and the bottom full! Mother had obviously not understood the concept of a short push of the button, so I explained it again before removing the (new) full cassette and setting off to empty it.

As we set off on the next stage of our little journey I reflected on the changes in my mother as she had grown older. She had seemed to cope with the advancing years very well until fairly recently, I thought. Or was it just that over the last few years I had seen less of her than previously and the changes seemed greater? Certainly she did not leave her house as often as she used to, probably because she only had herself to look after now, and had fewer reasons to venture out. Also, as is the case with all of us as we get older, her joints were becoming a little less mobile and her previously boundless energy was becoming less boundless. Then there was her increasing deafness. She would admit that she was a little hard of hearing but the truth was that it was becoming very hard for her to hear very much at all, and she flatly refused to wear the hearing aid that her doctor had prescribed for her. This was, in no small part, due to her friend Mary, who was also quite deaf. Mother and Mary were from the same part of Ireland and had been friends for many years and were very close friends for most of their lives. As their respective deafness grew more acute Mary managed to persuade her doctor to prescribe a very expensive hearing aid for her, while mother's doctor decided that a less expensive one would suit her; and consequently she felt that hers was inferior and refused to use it. I decided that this was the cause of the misunderstanding with the toilet and when explaining its use before leaving Cosgrove I took great care to ensure that she heard me correctly this time, and I was confident that she now fully understood the operation of said apparatus. As has often been the case over the years, events were to prove me wrong again.

Oblivious to the impending problems which were to manifest themselves over the next few days, we cruised on through Wolverton and Milton Keynes, myself at the helm, Pam ferrying sustenance back and forth and mother sitting on the front deck smoking her cigarettes and enjoying the views. As we moored for the evening Pam advised me to check the toilet as mother had used it again during the journey.

Now those of you who are used to my ramblings will have probably guessed what is to come, but I was absolutely confident that I had been able to impart to my mother the information which would allow the correct operation of the waste disposal equipment (toilet). Wrong! On inspection I found that it was in its previous state with the top tank empty and the bottom tank very full. At this point I decided that this was a battle I could not win, so I took the decision to just continue emptying the toilet waste at every opportunity and hope that mother did not need to use it too often.

Apart from the frequent emptying of the cassettes the rest of the weekend passed without incident and we were soon making our way back to our moorings at the marina, having stopped yet again to deal with another full cassette at Cosgrove on the way. As we tied up at our mooring Pam advised me that she had changed the cassette herself on the way because mother had used the facilities again, with the usual consequences. When we had finished mooring I took the full cassette to the car in order to take it back to Cosgrove to empty it yet again.

On my return we had some lunch and drove mother home, having a good laugh about the events of the last few days on our way back, deciding that it would be a tale we would tell to our grandchildren. How were we to know that this was not to be the end of this little saga?

A week went by and the events of the previous journey were almost forgotten as we made our way out of the marina with our two children on board, intending to spend a nice relaxing weekend in Milton Keynes, including a walk into the town from Campbell Park in order that we could go to the cinema. As I had been working that morning it was late afternoon before we left and it was decided that we would moor at Wolverton that evening and have a meal at the Galleon pub. As we passed through Cosgrove Pam asked whether we were going to stop at the sanitary station and it was at this point that I realised that I had left the spare toilet cassette in the boot of the car.

"No problem" I said "no one has used the toilet since last weekend, we'll be fine". Oh dear how wrong I was to be!

Everything went well during the evening as we moored and had our nice pub meal, and settled down for the night. Suddenly things took a very unexpected turn for the worse when our daughter, Michelle, said: "Dad" (isn't it funny how it's never mum when a disaster strikes) "the toilet's full".

At this point I must admit that I thought that I had been transported to a parallel universe. After all I knew that no one had used the toilet since the previous outing and that it had been empty when we left the boat. Then a horrible thought struck me. While I had gone to Cosgrove to empty the cassette the previous weekend Pam and mother had walked the short distance to our house in the village. Pam must have thought I was becoming deranged as I said to her

"Did you leave my mother unattended at any time last weekend?" Suddenly the penny dropped as she said

"I left her on the boat for a minute as I carried a few bits to the jetty". I didn't need to ask the next question, the full cassette telling its own story. She nodded sheepishly when I asked:

"Was she alone long enough to use the toilet?" This answered the question of the full cassette but a more immediate problem had become alarmingly obvious. At about eleven o'clock at night how were we to deal with this dilemma, with the empty one still in the boot of the car? After more than a few drinks at the pub I didn't feel confident enough to move the boat in the dark. Then I remembered someone telling me that the old boaters sometimes dealt with this situation by digging a small hole behind the towpath hedge and depositing the waste into it. Before there could be any argument I decided that this would be a good course of action to extricate ourselves from our predicament, so we quietly untied the boat and pulled it through the bridge hole to the deserted section of canal beyond. A few minutes later I had dug a small hole in the bank beyond the towpath and emptied the contents of the cassette into it, filling it in carefully to hide the evidence. As I walked back to the boat our son, Iain, excitedly pointed something out to me.

"That bank's turning blue" he said, pointing to where I had just been. My heart sank as I turned to look realising with despair that, whilst the old boaters may have been able to "bury the evidence", in the intervening years we had started to add chemicals to aid the breakdown of the cassette's contents, hence the sudden strange colour of the bank. Panic struck as I realised the implications of our latest predicament. After all it would not take Einstein to fathom out where the soggy blue mess had come from, our boat being moored right next to it.

"Quick" I said "move the boat". My family looked at me in alarm, assuming that the last vestiges of sanity had deserted me, and stood rooted to the spot.

"Quick" I screamed, lowering my voice to a panic stricken whisper as I realised I might be heard from the pub "undo the ropes, we've got to move the boat!" They were spurred into action as they realised what I meant and we frantically untied the ropes and started to pull the boat away from the crime scene, not stopping for almost a mile.

After mooring we tried, unsuccessfully, to get a little sleep but found ourselves up very early. We decided to set off anyway and soon found ourselves at Campbell Park, where we moored and spent the weekend as planned. On our return journey it was not hard to spot the area where our little disaster had occurred, a group of people gathered at the site, no doubt wondering what had caused the recent discolouration to the soil. We, who knew the answer, would have to remain silent about our knowledge. Until now.

Chapter 18

Of Soap and Penguins...

At first glance, this last item might seem out of place in this collection of tales. However, I make no apology for including it – there is a boating connection, even if it is somewhat obscure, even tenuous. It was written in July 2009, during a trip with the historic pair Nutfield and Raymond, its author reclining on the cabintop of the Raymond; and I have photographs to prove it! The hand-written drafts were given to me, and I found them irresistibly engaging, the offbeat, nonsensical humour very reminiscent of Spike Milligan.

Another friend of mine concurred with my opinion, a man of some perspicacity; and with this volume in preparation for publication, I couldn't resist including it, I hope, to your amusement. I hope you will also agree that this is nonsense poetry at its best – all the more astonishing, then, that the author has even now yet to reach his thirteenth birthday.

Geoffrey Lewis, October 2009.

See over:

Of Soap and Penguins, and Decaffeinated Sheep

By Gabriel Meurer-Wilde

When you roll the slippery soap
Down the old slippery slope
Don't forget to hide
In the teapot down the side
From the ringle dingle dangle
Who will get you in a tangle
And the ping pong puddle
That will get you in a muddle.
Then look over the side
Where the penguins like to slide
Down the old slippery slope
Where you rolled the slippery soap.

There's a new slippery slope
To roll your slippery soap
'Cause the penguins on the side
Who often liked to slide
Down the old slippery slope
Simply couldn't cope
With the constant rolling soap.
So a new slope was created
To replace the old and dated
Version of the slope
Where people rolled their soap.

Of Soap and Penguins

The penguins which did slide
Over the side of the slippery slope
Were bemused and confuzzled
And extremely puzzled
When the decaf sheep came to town.
They watched and they watched
As the sheep climbed the slope
Just to slide all the way down.
The penguins got annoyed
So the sheep got buoyed
And moved to the new slippery slope.
So the penguins had won,
Another job done,
Just like they did to the soap.

Many sailors travelled
And many travellers sailed
To see the strange new wonder of the decaf sheep,
To watch it making products like coffee, coke and Jeeps.
But people didn't realise that this the sheep just did not like,
So they were all surprised when he suddenly went on strike,
And oh the crowds did miss him with his special decaf air
And the products like his decaf wool that they'd often
bought to wear.

As the decaf sheep
Sat on a sandy beach
Somewhere in south France
Suddenly crowds came to him
Asking for a decaf dance.
To them he did refuse,
Saying 'later, no, not now!'
So they sadly wandered off
And found a decaf cow.

Glossary of Terms

This isn't supposed to be any kind of complete list of 'boating' terms and expressions, so you won't find every strange word you've ever overheard in a canalside pub here! Rather, I've included it just so that the non-boaters or new boaters among you won't be totally flummoxed by some of the odd terms we've used in this book. I don't think I've missed any – if I have, you can always call the publishers, who will be just as puzzled as you are...

BARNEY BOAT	One of the first steel-hulled boats built for pleasure use by Braunston Boats Ltd in the 1960s and 70s, the name comes from their designer, Chris Barney.
BLADES	Boater's colloquial term for the propeller.
BOLINDER	The first internal combustion engines used on the canals were built by the Bolinder company in Sweden. Most were single-cylinder semi-diesels, requiring the use of a blow-lamp to heat them up before starting, and had no gearbox – the entire engine could be reversed, being of two-stroke operation. And that's a nice trick if you can do it, believe me.
BOW	The front (pointy) end of a boat, not commonly used on the canals – see FORE-END.
BRACKET	Boater's term for the throttle control – 'full bracket' means going flat out. The usual state in the days of the trade.

BREASTING UP   The process of tying a pair of boats side-by-side, for working through wide locks or tying up at night. Boats thus tied are referred to as 'breasted up'.

BREASTING STRING   A short rope, usually attached to a shackle on the butty's stern, which is used to snatch the boats together when breasting up.

BRIDGE NARROWS   The narrowing of the canal channel where it passes under a bridge. Often the narrows remain when the bridge has been demolished, causing some confusion.

BUCKBY CAN   A water-can supplied by the now-closed shop by Long Buckby top lock. These cans were regarded as the best available in the days of the canal trade, and were a source of pride and envy among the working boaters. Often used now, incorrectly, for any water-can of traditional design.

BUTTY   An unpowered boat towed behind a motor, able to carry about 30 tons. Most canal carrying was done with pairs of boats, allowing the maximum cargo to be moved by a small crew.

CABIN SHAFT   A short (6-8 foot) shaft kept on the cabin-top, with a spike and hook at one end, usually brightly painted. Useful for picking up ropes at a distance, or retrieving crew from the canal.

CANTS   Raised areas around the fore-ends, and the counter of a motor-boat. Smaller ones are sometimes used as handrails on the edge of the cabin roof.

CLUTCH — Just like your car! The clutch disengages the drive from the propeller shaft, controlled by a lever on a boat. Old boaters sometimes referred to 'forward clutch' and 'stern clutch' instead of forward and reverse gear.

COPINGS — Short-hand for 'coping stones', the top edge of the canal bank in locks or around bridges where it is built up.

COUNTER — The short round deck at the stern of a working or traditional type boat, behind the cabin.

CRATCH — A storage area at the front of a working boat's hold, behind the fore-deck, usually covered by a short canvas cloth over the erected deck-board and top-plank.

CROSS-STRAPS — Two short ropes used for towing an empty butty, which give a tight articulation between motor and butty, usually left on the butty's fore-deck when breasted in locks, ready for use.

CUT (THE) — Boater's colloquial term for the canals.

DECK-BOARD — A wooden structure roughly triangular in shape which is erected above the fore-deck to form the front shape of the cloths when covering a load which needed weather protection.

DOLLY — Point of attachment for ropes, usually for mooring. The ones on the fore-end or a butty's stern were often known as T-studs from their shape.

'ELLUM — Boater's term for the combination of rudder and tiller, used to steer a boat, derived from 'helm'.

EYE	Loop-shaped splice in the end of rope where it drops over the dolly or T-stud on the boat.
FEEDER	A channel or culvert where water is fed into the canal.
FENDER	A device used to cushion the boat (or the lock-gates, etc) from inadvertent contact, traditionally of woven rope.
FORE-DECK	The deck area immediately above the fore-end of the boat.
FORE-END	The front (sharp) end of a boat, usually preferred on the canals to the term 'bow'.
GUARD	Strip of steel, usually D-shaped in section, affixed around the stern and fore-end to protect the hull from damage, used on wooden and steel boats alike.
GUNWALE	The top edge of the hull, about 4-5 inches wide, along the side of a narrowboat's hold, and around the cabin on a motor-boat. A butty's cabin has no gunwale around it.
HATCH	A sliding cover above the cabin doors. To be 'in the hatches' refers to standing inside the doors, with the hatch open, to steer the boat.
HOLDING OVER	Steering to one side of the canal to avoid oncoming boats.
INVERTER	Device used on modern boats which converts DC current from the batteries to mains AC to power the TV, play-station, etc.
IRON TRUNK	Popular name for cast-iron aqueduct over the Great Ouse River between Cosgrove and Wolverton on the Grand Union.

JOSHER — Boater's term for the boats built and run by Fellows, Morton and Clayton Ltd, once Britain's biggest canal carriers, derived from the company's founding MD, Joshua Fellows.

LIFT BRIDGE — A movable bridge which is raised to allow boats to pass.

LINES — Another word for ropes, e.g. 'mooring lines'

LOCKS — A canal structure used to raise and lower boats from one level of the canal to another (as if you needed telling). They come in wide (14 feet, able to pass two narrowboats at once) and narrow (7 feet, one boat at a time!).

MOORING PIN — Steel pins about 12-18 inches long which can be driven into the bank to moor the boat to.

MOTOR
(or MOTOR BOAT) — The powered boat which tows the butty. With the weight of the engine, a motor can carry about 24 tons of cargo.

NARROWBOAT — In order to fit into narrow locks, the standard beam (width) of canal boats is 7 feet, and any such is referred to as a narrowboat. The term 'barge' should be avoided, as it is regarded as insulting by canal boaters.

PADDLES — The device used to let water in or out of locks. The visible parts on the gates or locksides are known as 'paddle-gear'. Bottom paddles are commonly in the gates, but top paddles are often in both the gate and ground beside the lock,

	where the water passes through culverts to fill the lock.
PAIR	Shorthand for 'a pair of boats', used of the old working pairs.
PALOMA	Once a common form of gas-fired water-heater in pleasure boats.
RANGE	Common term for the solid-fuel stove used for heating and cooking in working boat cabins.
SETTING AHEAD	The term for going ahead to set the next lock ready for the boats.
SHACKLE	A D-shaped device with a screw fixing used as a semi-permanent attachment for ropes or fenders.
SHAFT	Wooden pole used for moving the boat, e.g. pushing off from the bank or helping to turn around.
SINGLE OUT	Separating boats that have been breasted up, when leaving a wide lock. Boats running with the butty on tow are referred to as 'singled out'.
STEM POST	The central vertical rib which forms the point of the fore-end, the bit which hits the lock-gate when you get it wrong.
STERN	The rear (blunt) end of the boat.
STERN GEAR	Collective term for the tube and seal where the propeller shaft protrudes through the stern of the boat.
STERN TUBE GREASER	A device for pumping grease into the stern gear which helps to maintain the seal, thereby keeping the canal out of the boat.
STRING	Another term used for various pieces of rope on a boat.

SUMMIT — Not the Kilimanjaro, but the boater's term for the highest level of a canal, with locks descending from both ends.

TILLER — The 'handle' part of the steering gear, commonly used today for leaning on and posing.

TOP PLANKS — Planks which are laid along the stands over the hold of a working boat, from the deck-board to the cabin, which form the upper frame for the canvas cloths used to protect the load.

TOWPATH — Remember that the canals were first built for horse-drawn boats. Need I say more?

TYING UP — The more common canal term for mooring up.

ULTRA SOUND — Clever device for determining the thickness (or otherwise) of the steel in a boat's hull.

WATER CAN — Galvanised steel cans, usually 2 or 3 gallon capacity, kept on working boats to carry a supply of fresh water. Often highly decorated, some were highly prized (see Buckby Can).

WEED HATCH — A hatch in the stern of modern boats which allows access to the propeller to clear weeds or other obstructions from the blades.

WEIR — A point where water is allowed to run over from the channel, either to bypass locks or reduce the level of the canal.

WHARF — A place where boats were loaded or unloaded. Most have houses or supermarkets built on them now.

WINDING HOLE   A wide space in the canal which allows full-length boats to be turned around. Pronounced as in what you might do to a baby, not a clock.

'...this engrossing story... be warned, however, that it will certainly tug at your heart strings like the author's other books.'
Stan Holland, Canals & Rivers Magazine

These are the three titles of the popular Michael Baker trilogy which was completed in 2009 with *The New Number One*.

It all started when ten-year-old Michael Thompson had had enough. Mentally and physically abused by his drunken father, treated like a skivvy by his mother, he had taken all that his miserable life could throw at him; but then the final blow came when his dog was taken away as well: On a bitter cold night in January, 1940, he set out to commit suicide ¬ but all does not go according to plan...

The three books tell a story of England's canals through the Second World War and beyond. The pressure and the pain, the humour and resilience of the boating people. Tragic and heart-warming, this trilogy charts the progress of a job becoming ever more difficult, against the broader panorama of worldwide events.